A YANKEE FLIER
WITH THE R.A.F.

THE HAWK DROPPED UPON THE BATTLE WAGON BELOW.

A Yankee Flier with the R.A.F.   *Frontispiece (Page 120)*

A YANKEE FLIER
WITH THE R.A.F.

BY

AL AVERY

ILLUSTRATED BY

PAUL LAUNE

  This book, while produced under wartime conditions, in full compliance with government regulations for the conservation of paper and other essential materials, is COMPLETE AND UNABRIDGED

GROSSET & DUNLAP
PUBLISHERS   NEW YORK

CONTENTS

A YANKEE FLIER
WITH THE R.A.F.

A YANKEE FLIER
WITH THE R.A.F.

CHAPTER I

GLORY TRAIL

SWING music was blaring from the radio
set in the mess when Stan Wilson entered.
His blue eyes, which gleamed with a great
zest for living, gazed levelly around the
room. There was a look in them which had
been born of penetrating the blue depths of
Colorado canyons and, later on, at the limit-
less spaces a flier sees. As usual, a half-
smile, seemingly directed at himself, played
at the corners of his mouth. There was seldom a moment so danger-filled that Stan
Wilson could not laugh at himself.

Here he was, really a fugitive from his distant homeland, standing in the Royal Air
Force mess while outside the closely cur-
tained windows all of London lay under an
inky blackout, listening and waiting for the

1

whine of the bombers. Stan was to be a member of Red Flight, which had been taking on replacements so fast that even the Flight Lieutenant wasn't able to get chummy with his men before they left him.

Stan smiled as he looked over the group in the mess. He had met Judd, a plump youth who was unofficially known as "jelly bean"; McCumber, a silent Scot who seldom smiled; and Tommy Lane, who never ceased to whistle tavern tunes. At a reading table scanning a paper sat Irish Kelley whose dark face and hawklike features made him look like a real lead slinger.

A man he did not know sat at a low table with a cup of black coffee before him. He was slender and even though his uniform needed pressing it seemed to fit him like a glove. His blond hair was closely clipped and the cool, gray eyes he lifted to meet Stan's gaze held a hint of insolent mockery. This was March Allison, Stan knew at once. A crazy Flight Lieutenant who was fast making a name for himself by his savage fighting heart and his dizzy flying ability. Stan stepped toward the table.

Allison nodded to a vacant chair beside the table and Stan dropped into it.

"I'm March Allison," he said and his cool eyes moved over Stan with irritating boldness. The superior air of the Britisher provoked Stan, but he refused to show it because he did not intend to lose his temper.

"I'm Stan Wilson," he said, "the new member of Red Flight."

"Stan Wilson, Canadian test pilot?" Allison clipped the words off in a manner that was almost derisive.

"That's what my card shows," Stan said testily.

"You're a Yank," Allison snapped. Then he grinned and little wrinkles crinkled the corners of his eyes. "I can smell a Yank," he added.

"If you don't mind suppose we leave it as the card reads?" Stan said coldly.

"All right with me, old fellow," Allison answered. "Only I hope you're a faster flier than the planes the Yanks have sent us so far."

That nettled Stan. A picture leaped into his mind—the picture of a trim fighter plane with low wings, and two banks of Brownings on each side of a 2,000-horse-power radial motor. Stan had nursed several of those babies into the blue. He didn't have to close his eyes to remember the test flight card he had filled out.

"Climbed to 20,000 feet in six minutes. Performed two barrel rolls, three loops. Checked all controls in neutral. Fired all guns and checked temperatures of gun-warming units. Did a series of sharp dives with steady pull-outs." As Stan's thoughts wandered back he grinned into Allison's face. He had put a number of Spitfires through their paces and knew that they were mud hens compared to the new babies which would soon be coming over from the United States.

"You'll soon get one with 2,000 horses up ahead and then you'll junk your Spitfires and Hurricanes," he said.

Allison cocked an eye at him and grinned widely. "Do you suppose you and I will be hitting the glory trail then?"

"I figure I'll be around doing something," Stan answered and matched the Lieutenant's grin.

A mess corporal was standing near by hopefully fussing with Stan's chit book which had just been issued to him. Stan gave the corporal a nod.

"Black coffee," he ordered.

At that moment Tommy Lane strolled over and flopped into a chair. He winked at Stan as he elevated his lank legs to the top of the table, almost upsetting Allison's coffee.

"If the notch don't get you the Messerschmitts must," he hummed softly. He seemed to be trying to tease Allison. When the Flight Lieutenant failed to show any interest, Tommy said, "Your treat, Allison. I'll have black coffee with a big jug of cream on the side."

Allison ordered Tommy's drink and watched the corporal mark it up in his chit book. He rolled an eye lazily toward the lanky youth.

"Stan Wilson from Canada," he drawled.

Stan grinned at Tommy Lane. His eyes bit into Allison. He did not like the way Allison was acting about his past record. If he was to have his chance to get a whack at the Jerries in this war, it was important that he be considered a subject of the British Empire, and he had come a lot of miles to get that chance.

All his plans would be ruined if the truth about him came out. Posing as a Canadian he had a good chance to get by, but there would be embarrassing questions about his past if his true nationality was found out. Questions that Stan Wilson couldn't answer without having his new officer's commission stripped from him. He waited breathlessly to see if Tommy would notice the challenge in Allison's voice, but the tall youth merely grinned cheerfully and said:

"We get darn good men from Canada."

Suddenly the intersquadron speaker rasped and began snapping orders. Every man in the room stopped talking and listened. A sudden tenseness filled the air of the room.

"Red Flight, all out! Red Flight, all out!"

"Well, well. Out for a breath of night air," Allison drawled. No one else said anything and the men of Red Flight barged toward the door.

"Green Flight, stand by," rasped the speaker.

Stan moved out behind Tommy Lane with Allison striding ahead. In less than three minutes they were bundled in flying suits, with parachutes batting their legs. Like waddling Arctic explorers they shoved out into the damp blackness of the night.

On the cab rank three Spitfires were shuddering under slow throttle. Flight sergeants were clambering down after warming up the motors. The ragged flare of exhausts whirled grotesque shadows across the ground, and oil fumes mixed with raw gasoline sucked up into their faces.

Sidders, Recording Officer, waved a sheaf of papers at Allison as he halted before the Flight Lieutenant. Sidders looked like a big bear with his greatcoat muffled around him. "Take the notch at 2,500. Landing signal, K. Good luck."

Allison grinned as he saluted. "Landing signal, K," he repeated mechanically.

A moment later Allison was jerking his hatch cover back and pinching one wheel brake. He rammed the throttle knob up and swung the Spitfire around. It lurched away and his voice came through the earphones of Tommy Lane and Stan Wilson.

"Slide up, Lane, Wilson." His voice was cold and impatient.

The three Spitfires shoved their noses into the black wall of the night, their exhausts snarling flame. They hesitated, waiting for the take-off signal.

"Check your temperatures," Allison droned into his flap mike.

Stan Wilson settled himself against his crash pad and got his chute squared under him. He had taken up his belt a notch beyond what he thought was possible. Tension gripped him. This was combat with a flaming trail ahead. He wasn't test diving and stunting now, he was hunting and would be hunted. And up there the night was as black as the inside of a cellar.

They got the clearance signal and the tails of the Spitfires lifted with a blast of prop pressure. They slid down the runway, gathering terrific speed. A few seconds later they were screaming over the blacked-out city.

"Close, close, tight in," Allison's voice droned.

Stan saw below the gray rectangle that was Hyde Park Square. He watched the knifing flame that the searchlights stabbed into the black heavens as they probed and searched for the black bellies of the bombers. The dull rapping of anti-aircraft shells beating against the heavy dome above smashed back the roar of his motor. The ground boys would soon spread a muck of fire and bursting steel over London.

"Tight, tight, we're coming into the notch," Allison's voice warned.

Red Flight swept north now in a steep, battering turn. The notch was dead ahead.

"Shove in, Tommy. Don't try slicing a cable," Allison snarled. "Come in! Come in! Here we go!"

The Spitfires slid closer together, bunched like darting swallows, their flaming breath licking into the night. In a few seconds they would be out where they could spread and go into action. For the first time, since rubbing elbows with a Spitfire, Stan wondered how you bailed out of the roaring monster if it broke up going 350 miles per hour. He slid his thumb across the black gun button as he set his windbreaker's edge on a line with Allison's aileron slit.

Blood pounded in his ears and a chill eagerness laid hold upon him. He leaned forward and would have shouted. Allison and Tommy and the whole British Broadcasting System would likely get the benefit of it if he cut loose with a cowboy yell. He closed his mouth firmly and fixed his eyes on the aileron slit ahead. The 1,000-horsepower Merlin engine was throbbing, hurtling him up and into the night. He could feel the assuring Brownings in the wings, ready to spew a hail of lead at the enemy. He did not realize it but beads of sweat stood on his forehead.

He was glad he was coming out of the narrow channel of terror which was charted anew each week. The notch was guarded by unseen, steel cables, slender knives of spun death, waiting to slice through the wing of a plane like a knife cutting through hot cheese. Or to come coiling down upon any ship that struck them squarely. The hydrogen bloated monsters that held the cables aloft swayed and tugged, sometimes swinging the steel lines far out into the notch.

Out of this avenue the three Spitfires bored. When they were clear Allison's drawl came in clearly:

"Pick yourself a bandit."

Two blades of silver light knifed upward. They swept back and forth, then stopped, remaining straight up. This was a signal Allison understood perfectly.

"Four bandits, quarter left," he snapped.

Before Stan could lay over, Allison's Spitfire was hurtling across his hatch cover, zooming up at the droning bombers. A second later he sighted a big Dornier just as she lurched upward in a frantic effort to avoid Allison's Brownings.

A half-smile came to the lips of Stan Wilson. Everything they had said about March Allison was correct. He was a demon in the air. Stan shot his Spitfire up at the belly of the floundering Dornier. He had no time to play spectator. Pressing the gun button he felt the kick of his eight Brownings as they drilled away. Pinkish flames spurted from the mid-section of the bomber as it whirled about, sliding off on one wing with flames, red now, belching out of it. It turned over and four men tumbled out. Stan watched long enough to see their chutes blossom against the red glow of gunfire from below. He was glad that the crew had been able to bail out.

On his right Stan saw tracer bullets from Allison's guns. He made out a dark hulk twisting and turning, then the hulk was lighted as the Nazi craft went down in flames. He couldn't spot Tommy as he zoomed upward and in a split second he lost Allison. Circling, he throttled down and let the Spitfire cruise. A chill feeling gripped the pit of his stomach. This was new stuff for him. He was out in the darkness roaring in a steep circle, looking for another bomber, but mostly waiting to hear Allison's voice. He knew the unseen cables were swaying and reaching, eager to knife him or to snarl his plane. Losing a wing wouldn't be as bad as having the cable come down on you. If you tangle in a cable you can't bail out. Stan peered down at the muck of shellfire below. He knew he wouldn't be able to hit the notch without help from at least one of the veterans.

Then he saw a searchlight beam pick up a dark shape below. It was a bomber going down to unload. Stan nosed over and sent the Spitfire down in a screaming dive. The flaming field of muck leaped up to meet him and shells burst close. As Stan closed in on the dive bomber it suddenly seemed to explode in his face.

Instantly Stan knew the cables had gotten the bandit. Frantically, he pulled the Spitfire up and sent her roaring toward the ceiling. He sucked in his breath as he brushed past one of the bloated gas bags. That was a score for the Ack-Ack gunners and the ground boys. Then he heard Allison's voice, cool and cheerful.

"Come in close, Red Flight. Somebody got two bandits. Who got two bandits?"

Stan slid over and down, sure now of his position. Ahead, he spotted Tommy and then Allison. They rocketed down through the notch, as sure of the narrow pathway as though the noonday sun was shining on the cables. Stan ducked in on Tommy's tail and went home with them.

"Why ask silly questions," Tommy was shouting to Allison. "Allison got one, Wilson got one, the Ack-Ack boys got one. Tommy got nothing except Allison's Spitfire in his lap."

Allison's voice came back in a sarcastic drawl. "I just shut my eyes and cut loose. When I opened them, there was a bandit minus one wing. How about you, Wilson?"

Stan cuddled his flap mike and laughed. He was sure of himself now. He had hit the glory trail and could laugh at its terrors. "I just did potshooting. Later I'll clip off tails and wings for you."

"Later?" There was that mocking note in Allison's voice.

The recall signal was calling them in. They swung over the blacked-out city and headed for home. Ten minutes later they did a parachute walk into the briefing room. Brooks, Squadron Leader, eyed them wearily. He acted as though he hadn't had any sleep for a good many nights, which was about correct. The three pilots moved over to his high desk and reached for report forms.

"Everybody all right?" the Squadron Leader asked as he began filling out their time record.

"Fit as flying fish," Tommy answered, grinning broadly. "Me, I like balloons." He winked at Stan.

"Shut up," Allison snapped.

"What did you spend on yours?" Brooks asked, looking at Allison.

"Six or eight seconds in one burst," Allison answered.

"Hundred rounds," the officer jotted down. Then he looked at Tommy. Tommy nodded toward Stan.

"Eight or ten, I guess. I used a pretty long burst," Stan admitted.

"One hundred thirty rounds, eight seconds," the officer jotted down.

A few minutes later Stan strolled into the mess with Allison. He felt tired and would have gone to his cubicle only he wanted to see what the boys did when they came in.

"Black coffee, that's the thing for balloon nerves," Allison said and looked sharply at Stan. "It's on me." He waved a hand to the mess corporal and called. "Two, black." Facing Stan, with a glint of humor in his eyes, he said. "Not bad, old man, but you're a Yank and you learned to fly in a fighter. And I think you'd best break down and tell me about it."

"Sorry, but I can't think of a story you'd believe," Stan said and grinned to hide his uneasiness. Allison was sharp as a tack. He had it in his head that Stan was a Yank, which would have been all right except that no Yank needed to masquerade as a Canadian to get into the Royal Air Force. Not a flier like Stan Wilson.

They sank into chairs and waited for the coffee. Tommy hadn't showed up and they had the mess to themselves. Allison leaned forward.

"I think the old man has something special up his sleeve," he said. "When he acts tough and gets hard he's about to cook up a messy job. Want in on it if it comes?" He was grinning at Stan in his most derisive manner. He might just as well have added. "Of course you won't want in."

"Check me in," Stan said stiffly.

"Fine."   Allison leaned back and elevated his legs to the top of the table. "Fine. I figure the old man is going to give us a one-way ticket."

"A what?" Stan asked. The way Allison spoke made a chill run up his spine.

Allison turned his head and looked at Stan. "In the last war when fighters were sent out as scouts they had to come back to report. In this man's war they radio back their reports. After that they play tag with a swarm of Messerschmitt One-Tens."

"I see." Stan could well imagine what sort of tag three Spitfires would play with a dozen or more ME's. It was just plain suicide stuff. "Ever been on one?" he asked.

Allison grinned widely. "Once. A cloud, plus eight Brownings and a lot of fool's luck, brought me back with most of my ship. It beats hitting the glory trail every night."

"Sounds interesting," Stan agreed as he pulled his steaming cup of coffee to him and began dropping sugar lumps into it. "I aim to get a kick out of it."

Allison laughed. "Hanged if I don't believe you will. You'll go if I do any of the picking."

"And about this Yank business." Stan looked Allison squarely in the eye. "It isn't international. It isn't a violation of any of the laws of Britain or any country. It's a personal matter. If you keep on talking about it you'll lose a flier, that's certain."

"I see," Allison said, but he kept on grinning his superior grin. "I knew it wasn't anything rotten. Sorry I was nosey. It won't come up before anyone, Yank." He lifted his cup. "Here's to the glory trail!"

Stan joined him. Tommy came in and

sprawled out on a bench with his feet against the wall. He looked over at Allison and Stan.

"The O.C. says Green Flight is taking over for the rest of the night, so you birds can go to bed."

"Where are you going?" Allison asked.

Tommy uncoiled himself and stood up. He began humming a snatch of song, stopped abruptly and answered Allison.

"Too quiet around here for me." Without any further explanation he strolled out.

"That nut can't get action enough running the notch. He's on his way over to a bombing squadron. He'll talk the O.C. into letting him go on a bombing raid as a gunner." Allison got to his feet. "Me, I'm going to bed."

"Reckon I will, too," Stan answered.

CHAPTER II

STAN entered the mess room the next morning and stood looking around. There was the same air of indifference, with that undercurrent of tension. A dozen men were eating breakfast at the tables in the far end. They were all talking and joking, but at any moment they might be called to face the grim specter of death high in the clouds. Stan spotted Allison sitting by himself at a small table near a window. He looked about for Tommy but the lanky flier wasn't in the room. Probably sleeping in after an all-night party aboard a bomber, thought Stan.

He crossed the room and as he approached Allison he saw that the Flight Lieutenant's breakfast lay untouched before him. His coffee looked cold and stale. But it was the grimness of his face that jolted Stan. Allison looked up and there were savage points of light in his eyes. His mouth twisted into a sardonic grin.

"Sit down, Stan," he said, using Stan's first name, something he hadn't done before.

"What's up?" Stan demanded quickly as he slid into a chair.

"We're on day shift," Allison said. "Sunshine all the way."

"Where's Tommy?" Stan drove at the thought that had leaped into his mind.

Allison looked at him and his lips pulled into a thin line. "The kid picked up a package last night. A Falk-88 laid a shell right up against the Bristol and cracked her open."

Stan said nothing for a minute. He knew that the words of the Flight Lieutenant were likely the last he would say about Tommy Lane's last ride. Then something like red fire surged up inside him.

"We'll keep him in mind," he said grimly.

"I'll see that the score keeps even," Allison said and savage lights flickered hot in his eyes.

The mess corporal appeared with a private at his heels. "We have some very fine waffles," he said.

"Bring me black coffee," Stan growled.

"And waffles?"

"Sure, sure."

The corporal turned away. It worried him that his fliers were so temperamental they didn't eat enough of his food.

Allison shoved aside his cold coffee. "We have a new man coming in. He ought to be here any minute now."

Ten minutes later a tall man entered the mess. He stood looking around, then spoke to one of the privates. The soldier nodded toward Allison, and the tall youngster headed across the room.

"Here he comes," Allison muttered sourly.

Stan saw a black-haired, hawk-faced young man of perhaps twenty. The new flier had a big mouth that was pulled into a loose frown as his dark eyes stabbed about the room, pausing to rest for a moment upon each face. He walked with a swagger and his uniform was neatly creased. At first glance Stan didn't think much of him.

"Hello," he greeted Allison. "Are you Flight Lieutenant Allison?"

"Sure. Sit down and have something."

"I'm Arch Garret. The O.C. sent me over

to plug a hole in Red Flight. I'll take care of you boys." He glanced at Allison's sloppy uniform and then at Stan's, which was little better.

"That's nice of you, old man," Allison said in a soft drawl.

Then Arch Garret began to tell how good he was, and how many Messerschmitt One-Tens he had knocked off in coast combat. He spoke loudly so that all in the room could hear. After listening for a few minutes, Allison yawned and got to his feet. Without a word he walked away.

Stan was sure Garret hadn't had all the experience he claimed. One thing was certain: Stan knew the new flier would soon have the gang down on him. He listened silently to Arch Garret's talk while he finished his waffles and coffee.

"I'm from the United States," Garret said. "I was the best test pilot Lockheed ever had or ever will have. Spinning those Yank jobs was too slow for me. I had to have action." Garret smoothed a closely cropped little mustache and swelled out his chest.

Stan pretended to be dumb, but he was

looking Arch Garret over very closely. He knew every ace test pilot Lockheed had had in the past five years. He was sure Garret was lying.

He was about to ask some questions when the intersquadron speaker began snapping and clicking. A voice filled the room.

"Red Flight, all out! Red Flight, all out!"

"That's us," Stan said as he jumped to his feet. "Sorry, you'll have to miss your coffee."

Arch Garret's manner changed at once. He quit bragging and seemed to be a little nervous as he got to his feet.

"Where are we headed?"

"I don't know," Stan snapped.

They barged out of the mess close upon Allison's heels. Everything was rush, with parachutes to adjust and flying suits to climb into. Stan paid no more attention to Garret until they were outside.

The three Spitfires of Red Flight were throbbing with restrained power on the cab rank. Stan felt better about sliding into his cockpit because the sun was shining and he could see the silver wires attached to the hydrogen gorged balloons. This was better.

The flight sergeants had cleared the ships and Allison had gotten his orders from the recording officer. In another minute the lead Spitfire had cramped about and was sliding toward the line. Stan swung into place and watched Garret get set. The new flier slid his plane up to the line with showy flash, gunning and idling the big motor in a way that made Stan's nerves rasp. To him a motor was a living thing and he hated to see one abused.

"Steady, Red Flight," Allison was snapping into his flap mike. "Check your temperatures."

Stan called back his O.K. Garret did not clear. Allison's voice came in angry, cold.

"Are you set, Garret?"

"Sure, big boy, I'm always set," Garret replied.

"Then sound off as you should," Allison snapped.

A second later they were off, tails lifting, boring across the turf. With a wrenching lift, they bounced up and lifted into the blue where big clouds floated over the city of London. Allison's voice came in. The crispness was gone and the drawl was there again.

"Close formation, and keep it close all the way out. We're headed for emergency work below the Thames estuary. Junkers Ju 87's for breakfast."

The Spitfires closed in and roared away, gaining altitude as they bored into the early morning light. In a very short time the twisting streets, the masses of little squares that were blocks of buildings faded away below them. Allison took them up above the fleecy clouds and into the great, high-piled formations.

"Ought to find them sneaking around up here," he drawled.

Stan looked out upon the mountains of clouds and the patches of blue sky. The Junkers Ju 87's were dive bombers, popularly known as Stukas, and their presence meant a raid upon shipping.

"Red Flight, keep west by south. Red Flight, keep west by south." It was the control room at the field sending them directions from the big room with the table which had a huge map spread on it. On that map were toy planes which the watchers shoved about with wooden rakes.

Ahead, Allison broke out of the feathery edge of a cloud into a great valley of clear blue. Stan sliced through the cloud close beside him. Garret was trailing a little now.

"Three Stukas cruising, four points right," Allison grated. "Three Stukas. Don't let one of them get away or he'll come back again."

Instantly the Spitfires broke formation and Allison went plummeting down, his Merlin roaring wide open. His twisting flight was an amazing show of cold skill. Stan peeled off and shot after him. He was sure Allison had picked the Stuka on the right so he took the one on the left, leaving the center bomber for Garret, who wasn't getting in as fast as he should.

"Easy, a cinch!" Allison's voice roared out of Stan's headset. "Here's one for Tommy."

Stan saw his Spitfire lay over on her side and slice down upon the Stuka, her eight Brownings drilling flame and lead. The startled crew of the bomber immediately came to life. They had been craning their necks, looking for slow crawling freighters headed into port. They sent the Stuka into a nose dive, spewing bombs to lighten their load, but they were not fast enough. Stan saw the right wing of the big raider rise, then whirl away. The Stuka spun out of the square space in his windscreen doing grotesque loops.

Ahead lay Stan's target and his thumb pressed gently on his gun button as he roared down. His Brownings opened up and he saw the Stuka stagger and swerve as he thundered past in a hissing dive. Coming up he noticed that Garret's Stuka was streaking away toward the south with Garret making a feeble try at coming up under the big ship.

"Missed a dead target," Stan said grimly. "He hasn't fired a single burst."

Then Allison's voice cracked in over the air. "Messerschmitts up above in the big cloud. They're coming down. Seven in all." His words snapped off in a sputter of crackling static. Stan nosed up and saw the seven fighters diving upon Allison. Then he heard Allison's voice again.

"Better let me have them. Keep clear!"

Stan yelled into the flap mike. "Coming, Allison."

He gave the Spitfire all she had and the

Merlin wound up beautifully, lifting him up to meet the fighters diving out of the cloud above. As he went up he looked for Garret. At that moment they sure needed all of Red Flight. He spotted Garret diving for a great thunderhead.

"The scum," Stan snarled. He shot the words into the flap mike without realizing it.

It did not seem possible that Allison could escape from the deathtrap. The Stuka setup had been too easy after all. The Spitfires were twisting upward, straight on to meet the seven diving Messerschmitts, any one of which was near their match. Stan knew the boys at the controls of those ships were good fliers.

Allison's ship rolled over suddenly and fell away, then hit a steep spiral climb. For a few seconds it knifed along on its back. The maneuver threw the seven fighters off for a moment, giving Stan time to get more lift and more ceiling. Allison laid over in a vertical bank, and, as he swung back his guns, cut a swath across the enemy craft. One Messerschmitt went into a crazy whirl.

After that Stan was busy with his own end. He cut across the path of a streaking

fighter and sawed off his tail so neatly it
seemed to have vanished by itself. But the
next second he had a brace of roaring guns
in his face and the hatch cover above his
head shattered, showering him with glass
and pieces of metal. His engine did not fal-
ter as he stalled and slid off after the Nazi,
his Brownings ripping away. The fighter
dodged and twisted and got away, though it
was plainly hit.

As he dived to shake off another red-hot
gunner he saw Allison going straight at another Messerschmitt, the only one in his field
of vision. He waited for the burst from Allison's guns that would send the Nazi down,
but it did not come and Allison thundered
over the enemy ship, taking a ripping hail
of lead as he went.

"His guns are out," Stan groaned as he
sent his ship over in a roll and went down
after the raider, who was banking to dive
upon Allison's defenseless tail. Stan's lightning drop carried him down just in time to
drive the Messerschmitt away from Allison.
The crippled Spitfire ducked into a cloud.
Allison's voice came to Stan, mocking but
with his old drawl.

"Thanks, old man."

"Where's Garret?" Stan rasped back.

"I'm up here.   Just finished off my second bandit."

"You don't say," Allison cut in.   "Well, we're going in, boys, before we meet all of Goering's gang. If they're all as active as those Messers we just slipped away from, I don't care to tackle any more of them."

They settled into formation and dropped down upon London. The headset began to sputter and a voice from the ground said.

"Red Flight, come in.   Red Flight, are you all there?"

"All here," Allison called back cheerfully. He had recovered his sardonic good humor.

They slid up the Thames and on over the city to their field. Sliding in, Allison and Stan set down on an even glide. Garret slid in with a grandstand flourish. Stan eased in close beside him, clambered out of the cockpit and stepped across to Garret's Spitfire, giving it a searching look. His lips were twisted with anger as he caught up with Allison.

Allison gave him a wide grin. "Sweet going, Yank," he said softly.

"What got into your guns?" Stan asked in an effort to let his wrath cool.

"Got a burst through the center section. Those Jerries are liberal with their lead."

Stan saw that Allison was going to say nothing about Arch Garret's cowardly trick in cloud-sneaking when his pals were in a tight spot. He hitched along beside Allison, his parachute rapping him behind the knees. Garret had paused to show off before the ground crews. They heard him say, in a loud voice:

"I cut down on one Messer and then laid over just in time to take out another one."

Stan looked at Allison. He was grinning at Brooks who was chewing on a pencil and staring at him as if he had seen a ghost.

"Mead of Green Flight said seven Messers had you bottled, Allison," he said.

"Mead needs his eyes fixed," Allison answered as he slid out of his chute.

Squadron Leader Rainey came in. He had three rings of braid on his sleeve and wished he had only two so that he could be out on flight duty with the boys. In the last war Majors were flying men, but in this one they were just ground officers. His grim

face lighted in a thin smile as he looked at
Allison.

"Nice work, Red Flight," he said. "Like
to have been up with you."

"We could have used you, sir," Allison
said and laughed almost directly into Garret's face.

Garret had strutted to the desk just inside
the briefing room. He spoke loudly, paying
no attention to the Squadron Leader. He
leaned on the desk and fixed the briefing officer with a steady look.

"Chalk up a Stuka and two Messerschmitts for me. And add a note saying it
was lucky for two stiffs I was along."

Stan swung around facing Garret. The
gall of the man made his anger flare up and
he forgot all about regulations. "Why lie
about it," he said, his lips a tight line. "You
didn't fire a burst, you hid in a cloud. Next
time you better unlimber your guns while
you're in the cloud so you'll have an alibi."

Arch Garret's dark face twisted with rage.
"So you play that way, lying me out of
credit."

"I checked your guns before I came in.

You didn't fire a shot.'' Stan turned upon Allison and the Squadron Commander. As he did so he realized he had made a mistake. They were silently watching, their faces expressionless.

"Well then, Canuck, if you've checked my guns I'll pull down those credits," Garret snarled.

"You said something about my lying," Stan gritted as he swung around to face the flier. His six feet and two hundred pounds of muscular body made him look like a certain Colorado U. half-back who had once been picked as All-American. Stan wouldn't have admitted it, he wouldn't have dared, but he had once been a great blocking back.

Allison stepped forward. "You come with me, Wilson," he said. "I want to tell you a few things you ought to know."

The Squadron Leader nodded to Allison. He turned upon his heel without looking at Garret. Snarling, his lips twisted with anger, Garret made off to his cubicle.

In the mess Allison sank into a chair. He grinned across at Stan, who had seated himself. "Mind if I order tea? I've drunk a gallon of coffee just to be polite to you."

Stan grunted, "You don't have to be polite to me."

"I don't intend to from now on, old man." Allison's eyes were twinkling.

"What's on your mind? Regulations and such rot, I suppose." Stan was still hot under the collar.

"We don't do it that way here," Allison said. "A rotter like Garret is always taken care of."

"You mean he's out?"

"No, I can't swing that, but we don't have to have him in Red Flight." He reached for the cup of tea the corporal had set in front of him. "You made an enemy who will go a long way to stymie you."

"He'd better stay out of my way," Stan growled.

Allison grinned. "Guess he had, at that," he admitted.

CHAPTER III

BILL O'MALLEY

ALLISON leaned back in his chair and laughed softly. Stan waited for the Flight Lieutenant to explain his sudden mirth. Allison had just come from the O.C.'s office. He turned to Stan.

"I put in a call for a new flier. After all, I can't have a couple of prize fighters trailing me around. I got a very sweet fighting man. He doesn't love the English so much, and he doesn't hate the Jerries so much. He's an Irish boy whose ancestors haven't missed a war in a thousand years. He just couldn't stay out of this one." Allison chuckled and nodded his head.

Stan turned his gaze toward the door, which had swung inward revealing a tall youth.

"There," said Allison, "comes Bill O'Malley."

Bill O'Malley was long and lank, with an Adam's apple that bobbed up and down his throat. His bony shoulders were stooped in a most unmilitary manner, and his head boasted a thatch of flaming red hair. He was about the last person in the world Stan would have picked as a daredevil flier. His homely face and his sloppy figure would not have inspired fear or confidence in anyone. Allison waved to him.

"Hi, old fellow, come over and meet a pal."

Bill O'Malley grinned as he slouched across the room. As soon as his big mouth cracked into a smile Stan knew he was going to like this big Irisher.

Allison arose. He was acting with deliberate and mock politeness. "O'Malley, meet Wilson," he said with a sweep of his arm. Then the derisive mask slipped over his face and he seated himself again.

"Sure, 'tis a quiet an' homelike place ye have here, Commander," O'Malley said. "Wilson, me boy, I'm right glad to meet up with ye."

"Nothing ever happens around here," Allison agreed. "It's a peaceful place."

"Snug as a clambake," O'Malley agreed. "But much more dead. Now when I gave me word I'd come in with you boys the O.C. made quite a talk about how tough the job was. Here we sit like auld friends at a picnic." He scowled bleakly at Allison.

"I'll send over for a flight of Jerries," Allison said with a grin.

" 'Twill be a pleasure, me foine fellow," O'Malley answered. "I came over here to see some action."

Both Stan and Allison knew Bill O'Malley meant just what he said. He was wild as any crazy hare, but he had a name that was already on the tongues of ground men when spectacular stunts were talked about. Stan guessed that Allison had not had much trouble in getting the Irisher away from whatever flight he was with. Few Flight Lieutenants would have cared to be responsible for him.

The loud-speaker began to blare. "Red Flight, all out! Green Flight, all out! Yellow Flight, all out!"

"Sounds like the whole Jerry outfit is on the way," O'Malley said as he unwound himself from a stool and made for the door.

There was no mistaking the fact that O'Malley was a first-class fighting man. Stan knew it by the way he got into his Spitfire and rammed the hatch cover home. By the time they had zoomed up and away, he was sure of it. Allison was chuckling over the radio.

"Cuddle in, Red Flight. We pick up Bristols and Blenheims at 10,000."

" 'Tis no wet nurse I'll be," came the Irish brogue of O'Malley. "I resign this minnit."

"Headquarters says the Jerries have two dozen Messer One-Nines on a reception committee," Allison droned back.

"The spalpeens! Why such a measly little bunch?" O'Malley demanded indignantly.

Stan gave his attention to flying. The squadron droned into a thick bank of clouds and was swallowed. Nine demons bored ahead to take a bombing flight through.

"Rose Raid, take position. Rose Raid, take position," came a voice over the air from the tactics group gathered around a big map at headquarters.

Stan grinned. The British were odd in many ways. For no good reason, they called this raid Rose Raid instead of B-7 or some other businesslike tabulation. Then he sighted the bombers 1,000 feet below. Three heavily loaded Bristols and three Blenheims. Stan remembered the fast-flying Consolidateds and the B-19's of the United States Army. Soon, if he was lucky enough to stay alive, he might be escorting B-19's.

Up and up they went into the clouds, with the bombers droning steadily southeast and the Spitfires cruising above and below and around.

The radios were all strangely silent now. There was no talk and Stan let his ears fill with the pleasant roar of his Merlin. He bent forward and stared at his instrument panel. That gauge couldn't be right, it must be jammed or something. If the needle was reading right he had less than a half tank of gas. He bent forward and rapped the panel. The needle did not change, except to surge a bit further toward the empty side. Stan's mouth drew into a grim line. He could believe that gauge and turn tail—or he could figure it was wrong and go on.

If it was right, he was short of gas for the trip. A hard gleam shone in his eyes. Regardless of the gauge, his tank should have been filled full. If it hadn't been filled there was dirty work somewhere. He thought of Garret. Allison had said Garret had been put on the ground. Stan wondered what job Garret had been given.

Then he snorted. He was letting himself go. Just because he was sore at Garret he was imagining things. He rapped the dial sharply and the needle jumped, then settled back. If he went on he would run out of gas over German territory and have to go down. In spite of himself, he couldn't help muttering:

"That would be a nice way of getting rid of me."

He shrugged his shoulders. Allison was dipping his wings in a signal. They were going down to have a look below. He couldn't use his flap mike. If he cut and ran he would have to prove he hadn't drained his tank to get out of a hot odds-on battle; he'd have to have proof that the tank wasn't filled when he took off. But he had to decide at once.

A guarded voice spoke. It was Allison's. "Peel off and dive by position. Come up after a check below clouds."

The Flight Lieutenant's Spitfire lanced over on its side and streaked down like a rocket. O'Malley followed. Stan's lips pulled into a hard line. He flipped the Spitfire over on its side and went roaring down the chute. The air speed and altimeter were going insane. The shriek of the dive shook every nerve in Stan's body, and set him back against the crash pad, holding him there with a powerful grip. The three Spitfires roared out of the clouds at the same instant. They streaked into the clear blue for a moment, then shot upward and ducked back into the cloud again.

They had seen nothing except a low and rocky coastline with white lines of breakers beating against it. Not a plane in the world, except the squadron, so it seemed.

And then the clouds broke away and a harbor was in the frame of their windscreens. It looked like a toy harbor with its oblong breakwater. A great hangar with a black painted roof looked out upon the gently rolling waters. There were seaplanes in the picture somewhere. Stan craned his neck and saw what was holding the eyes of the men in the Blenheims and the Bristols.

Three toy boats rode at anchor beside a dock. Those were supply ships that had slipped through the blockade. Headquarters was taking a last desperate chance of keeping that valuable cargo from getting through.

Then the Rose Raid actually started. The radio began to crackle. "Rose Raid at targets! Rose Raid over targets!" That was the squadron leader telling headquarters they were going down.

The nine light Spitfires went down in a screaming dive to cover the Blenheims and the Bristols. The big Bristols swung into line-astern formation and bashed through the first upheaval of Flak-88 shells. Black and white blooms of bursting shells bracketed them as their leader slid into the curtain of fire. The next instant the big Bristol disappeared in a mass of smoke and flame.

A Blenheim on Stan's right twisted upward, threw away a wing and went down in a dizzy spin, ramming its nose into the roof of the black hangar.

The remaining four bombers plunged down upon their objective with the Spitfires doing dizzy stunts alongside them and the air seemingly filled with Heinkel single-seaters which had slashed into the picture from nowhere. A darting Heinkel dived upon Stan. Stan opened up and saw an aileron flutter away from the plummeting fighter. The formation of Spitfires had broken up now. It was everybody into the dogfight to keep the Heinkels from getting at the four precious bombers.

The slashing, whirling Spitfires did the job. They tore into the Heinkels and their deadly eight-gun combinations showed at once what superior fire power they had. Stan watched O'Malley send a fighter down and slide over on his back, out of the path of three more, to get another before his first burst of fire had ceased smoking. O'Malley was a demon of the sky. He was in and out and up and down and his trail was a trail of death. Allison was up there, too, doing just about as well but doing it with cold precision rather than by sheer recklessness.

Stan knifed into a wedge of Heinkels darting down to drop upon one of the Bristols. The Heinkels scattered before his fire, twisting and ducking and darting. Stan laid over and looked down. The bombers had unloaded. Below him the three ships, big now, and dirty in their streaked gray and black paint, were very close. Men were running wildly about on their decks or leaping into the water. One of them burst into flame amidship, another seemed to explode, the third listed far over and her stern sank slowly down.

Stan's radio was shouting at him. "Rose Raid! Rose Raid! Ten bandits down. Two bombers have left formation. Two fighters have left formation. Rose Raid, come in. Rose Raid, come in!"

The Spitfires could not come in. While the bombers slipped away under full throttle, free of their loads and faster than they had been, the Spitfires slashed and blasted and ducked. Stan watched a Spitfire go into the bay, twisting and spinning. He wondered if it could be Allison or O'Malley.

"Red Flight, come in." That was Allison's voice.

"Comin' soon as I get me another spalpeen," O'Malley's brogue burred.

Stan glanced at his gas gauge. It showed empty, but the Merlin was still hammering away. He nosed her up as he cuddled his flap mike.

"Wilson coming in."

Up and up the Spitfire roared, shaking the Heinkels off her tail as she twisted and banked, her 1,000 horses tossing her toward the ceiling. Stan held his breath as he headed her home. Was that gas gauge a liar?

He heard the Merlin cough and knew the gauge had not lied. Looking back he saw the dim outline of the enemy shore. Back there he could cripple down and they would not shoot him. They would be glad to get a sound Spitfire and they would keep him locked up for the rest of the war. Ahead lay the gray waters of the English channel, rough and sullen, cold as ice.

"Wilson out of gas. Making a try for home," he shouted into his flap mike.

Above him he saw that Messerschmitt One-Tens had joined the Heinkels in trying to finish off the Spitfires. He leveled off as the Merlin gave its last gasp of power and sent the ship gliding toward home.

For a time Stan thought the Jerries had missed him, they were so busy up above. Eight thousand feet below his wings the rough waters of the channel were moving up

to meet him. The first warning Stan had
that he was not to escape without a fight was
a terrific jolting and ripping that almost
shook him loose from his seat; the next was
the staccato rattle of a rapid-fire cannon that
was ripping great chunks out of his right
wing.

The Spitfire writhed up on her side, then
rolled over on her back and shot seaward.
Stan pulled the stick back against his stomach and kicked the right rudder viciously.
He looked up just as the Jerry loosed another broadside which missed the ship. The
Jerry zoomed back up, satisfied he had finished the Spitfire that was trying to slip
away.

Stan gave the Jerry but a glance. He was
battling to pull the Spitfire out of the spin
he had jammed her into. He soon realized
that there was no control left in the ship, so
he unbuckled his belt and rammed back what
was left of the hatch cover. He squirmed
out of the cockpit and dived. As he slid
away from the ship he felt himself caught
and held. His chute bellied out and the
shoulder straps wrenched at him. A second
later he was ripped loose and whirled away

from the crumpled wreck. As he leveled off he saw that he was about 3,000 feet from the water.

It appeared also that Stan had the channel to himself. Overhead he could hear the faint drone of motors; otherwise there was no sound except the cries of a half-dozen excited gulls that swooped down about him curiously as the chute let him drift downward toward the gray sea.

An inshore wind whipped at his clothing, twisting him dizzily as he dangled there in mid-air, and he had a brief, crazy hope that it might carry him in to land before he went down. But that wild hope died at once when he realized the shore was miles away.

There was nothing for it but to take his wetting and hope the R.A.F. life jacket was as good as it was supposed to be. He stared downward at the choppy surface that seemed to sweep upward to meet him, gritting his teeth to drive fear away. This was a chance every channel flier took . . . and sometimes they were rescued.

He handled the chute controls skillfully, easing himself down with the wind while he fought to loosen the buckles that held the straps tightly about him. If he went into the water with that chute dragging him down there wouldn't be any chance of eventual rescue.

As his numbed fingers tore at the buckles he wondered what it felt like to drown. The sea was close now. A bleak gray expanse of waves that reached hungry arms upward to receive another human sacrifice. One buckle came free, then another. He ripped himself out of the harness and plummeted down the last ten feet, his body driving deep into the icy cold water.

He came to the surface sputtering and beating the water madly, then remembered the life jacket he wore, and let its buoyancy support him while he took stock of the situation.

It looked hopeless. He was a single tiny speck floating on a vast expanse of sea where every surface craft was subject to attack and more intent on making port than searching for downed fliers. The sky overhead was clear of planes now. He wondered if anyone had seen him bailing out. He had reported he was short of gas. If either Allison or O'Malley made it back safely, he had a hunch they wouldn't rest until they returned to search the sea for him or the wreckage of his plane.

That was his only hope. Any other rescue would be purely accidental. The icy fingers of the water were eating into his flesh. The heavy flying togs were becoming water-soaked, dragging him down. He didn't know how long he could hold out. He tried to swim toward the dimly distant shore line, but the waves battered him back and the numbing cold stole away his strength.

He forced himself to relax, let the life jacket support him. It might be hours before rescue came. It looked hopeless, but a man never gave up hope while life remained in his body. If he could keep his head above water, keep from swallowing too much of the salt sea, he could last a few hours at least.

And he clung to the belief that Allison or O'Malley would return to look for him. Though he didn't know just what either of them could do if they did spot him from the sky. If one of them could get hold of a sea-plane he didn't doubt that they'd try to set

it down on the rough surface to rescue him.
He tried to recall whether he'd seen any seaplanes since arriving in England.

Things were getting hazy in his mind. He
gave up trying to move his limbs. The blood
was congealing in his veins. He had a
strange feeling that his flesh was becoming
brittle with cold, that he would break into
pieces if he tried to move an arm or leg.

A delightful sensation of helpless lethargy
crept over him. This was the sort of thing
he had read happened to people when death
was very close and inevitable. It was Na-
ture's kind way of drugging the perceptions
against the impact of death.

He began to hear a buzzing in his ears, and
he decided that was the beginning of the end.
It didn't matter now. Nothing mattered.
Not even the war.

The buzzing grew louder and became a dis-
tinct annoyance. He tried to shut it away
from his consciousness, but it persisted. He
felt himself being dragged back from the
coma into which he had sunk. The buzzing
became a loud drone, then smashed at his ear
drums with a shattering roar.

He came to life again, and fought to blink

his salt-encrusted eyelids open. He recognized that roar of a Spitfire motor. It was zooming over him, flattening out in a crazy reckless pancake dangerously close to the surface of the water.

He got one eye open and caught a flashing glimpse of a grinning Irish face leaning over the side of the plane and shouting something to him. The plane lifted swiftly and swept away and Stan found himself waving a numbed hand after it.

The ice in his veins was transformed into tongues of flame that licked through his body. O'Malley had come, just as he had known the Irishman would. He would bring a rescue ship back. All Stan had to do was stay alive a little longer.

He grinned happily as he watched the Spitfire become a dim speck in the sky and then disappear. He began beating the water with his arms and legs, and he jeered good-naturedly at the sea that had sought to engulf him.

The plane was coming back, circling high overhead to spot the floating pilot for a fishing boat that was putting out from shore. As the small craft drew near Stan saw two men in oilskins waving to him. He waved back, and then a strange thing happened. It was as though someone had struck him on the head with a sledge hammer. He was unconscious when the boat reached him, and he stayed unconscious for a full twenty-four hours.

He woke up in a strange new world that was utterly different from anything he had known before. A clean, white, antiseptic world with narrow beds and pretty girls in white uniforms. He was tucked in one of those beds, and one of the pretty girls in a white uniform was bending over him solicitously.

"Where am I?" he demanded.

"This is a hospital. You are very sick," the nurse said soothingly.

"Hospital!" Stan sputtered. "I'm not staying in any hospital. I was never in a hospital in my life!" He got to his feet as orderlies and a head nurse came running.

"Lie down or I will report you," the head nurse said severely. "You are sick."

"How long do you think it takes me to get over a bath?" Stan shot at the nurse.

"You'll be here two weeks," the head nurse informed him.

Stan had visions of Allison sending out for another man to fill the trio on Red Flight. He wrapped the blanket tighter around him.

"Get my clothes," he ordered.

"Get an officer," the head nurse snapped to an orderly.

Stan knew it was time for action. He swept the blanket ends off the floor and dived down the hall with the nurses running after him. A doctor came out of a room, looked at Stan, then ducked back quickly. Stan bounded down a wide stairway and out through a pair of open doors. People stared at him as he rushed up the street in his bare feet looking for a cab.

On a corner he bumped into two bobbies. They closed in on both sides of him.

"Easy, my man," one of them said. "Easy, now. We'll see you safe back to your bed."

"Fine," Stan answered. "Get me over to Merry Flying Field as quick as you can."

The bobbies looked at Stan then exchanged glances. He looked perfectly healthy and very powerful, though he was a bit pale and had a wild look in his eye. They nodded their heads.

"I'm from Red Flight over at Merry Field. Get me there and the Flight Lieutenant will vouch for me," Stan urged as he looked down the street and saw an ambulance rocking around a corner.

The bobbies were satisfied that this young giant was crazy and they had better humor him. They shoved him through the curious crowd that had formed on the corner. Within a few minutes he was seated in a cab bowling across the city.

Allison was lounging at a table drinking tea with O'Malley when two bobbies and a disheveled man wrapped in a wool blanket marched into the mess. They both leaped to their feet and rushed across the room.

"Stan, old chap!" Allison shouted.

"By the scalp of St. Patrick!" O'Malley boomed. "An' I thought you would drown sure before the boat got to you."

The bobbies nodded their heads and grinned broadly. They lifted their sticks and moved out, well satisfied with their work. Stan called after them:

"If you meet an ambulance wandering about tell the driver to go back to the hospital and give my regards to the head nurse." He sank into a chair and grinned up at his friends. "How about some clothes?"

"Coming right up. You can borrow my dress uniform," Allison said. "O'Malley insisted we hold off replacements for another day. The hospital said you'd be laid up for weeks, but O'Malley had a hunch you wouldn't let them keep you."

Stan told what had happened. When he had finished O'Malley beat a bony fist on the table.

"Faith, an' I think the gas business is a trick of that rotter, Garret. What he's after needin' is a good taste of me fist," he bellowed.

"We have no proof. If one of you fellows beat him up we'd all be grounded, you know," Allison cut in.

"If Garret was on the crew that handled the fueling that's enough for me," Stan said grimly.

"He was put in charge of our hangar by the O.C. But you can bet he covered his dirty work carefully. We'll just have to trap him." Allison spoke grimly.

"And in the meantime we better check our ships before we go out each time," Stan said. "If I'd done that this time I'd have brought my Spitfire back whole and wouldn't have had to take a bath in the channel."

"I'll bet the spalpeen will get a scare when you walk into that hangar," O'Malley said with a grin.

Stan got to his feet. "I'm going out there just as soon as I get some clothes. I warn you, O'Malley, this is my fight. You stay out of it."

O'Malley's eyes glittered. "I niver could stay out of a good scrap, but if you wade into him I'm thinkin' there won't be anything left for me to do but pick up the pieces."

"You better keep a tight hand on your temper, old chap," Allison warned.

"I will. I'll have the low-down before I sock him," Stan promised.

A half-hour later, dressed in one of Allison's uniforms, and looking little worse for his ducking, Stan strolled into the hangar.

Garret was not about so he went to the crew
that had handled his ship. They were really
glad to see him, he was sure of that. He
looked them over and had a feeling none of
them had had any part in the plot.

"Who gassed my Spitfire before she went
out on the last raid?" His eyes moved from
man to man.

A corporal stepped forward. "I did,
sir."

"Was the tank full when you rolled her
out?"

"Yes, sir. I rechecked. She was full up."
The corporal was positive.

"Did you gas her up immediately before
the flight?"

"No, we always gas up as soon as the Spits
come in, so they'll be ready without delay.
Sometimes they go right back up."

Stan nodded. He had known that.
"Was the squad out for breakfast?"

A sergeant spoke up. "Yes, sir. Lieutenant Garret sent us all out together. Squad
Four was on duty down the line and could
keep an eye on things and shove out for us
if a call came."

"He went with you?"

"Yes, he walked as far as his mess with us."

Stan smiled. "Thanks," he said. "My gas turned out a bit short and I got a ducking in the channel."

He saw the men begin eying each other when he said that. He turned and walked away. Garret had fixed himself a slick alibi. Stan was sure he would have little luck cracking it. As he neared the door Arch Garret entered.

"Hello, Garret," Stan said and grinned.

Garret stared at him for a minute, then his dark face flushed and his eyes gleamed with smouldering anger. He stepped closer to Stan.

"You think you can railroad me clean out of this man's army, but you'll get yours, and I'll be back in the air again."

"If any other funny things happen to my ship I'm going to take a poke at that pretty face of yours," Stan said.

Garret quickly backed away and hurried into the hangar. Stan walked across the square to his mess. Garret was a dangerous fellow, there was no mistake about that, and he hated Stan Wilson. Stan had a feeling, too, that Garret was going to make good on his threat.

He wasn't sure how Garret intended to do it, or how much the fellow knew, but there was no doubt he was a dangerous antagonist. And Stan had an uncomfortable feeling that Garret knew or at least suspected the truth about a certain phase of Stan Wilson's past that Stan had hoped he could leave behind him when he came across the sea to fight the Nazi war machine.

But that, he grimly told himself, was too much to hope for. No man can ever wholly escape his past. Fate has a way of stepping in and smashing the best-laid plans of humans. And Stan had a premonition that Fate had selected Arch Garret as its instrument to ruin his careful plans.

CHAPTER IV

NEW QUARTERS

O'MALLEY sat at a table with a whole pie before him. He sliced it neatly across, then turned it half around and sliced it across again. Allison snorted his contempt while Stan watched, a grin on his face.

"Niver be it said an O'Malley is hoggish. Will ye have a wee slab o' pie, Mister Wilson or Mister Allison?"

"Thanks, no," Stan answered. "I'm carrying all the ballast I can handle right now."

"I say, old chap, could that be the second or is it the third pie you've had this afternoon?" Allison cocked an eye at O'Malley whose big mouth was open to receive almost half of one piece of pie.

O'Malley munched the pie. " 'Tis but the third, Commander, and niggardly pies they make, too. Take the pies Mrs. O'Malley

makes, now they are pies." He grinned as
he slid his hand under another quarter of pie.

At that moment an orderly appeared and
handed Allison a slip of paper. Allison read
it and scribbled a notation on it, handing it
back to the orderly.

"Nothin' iver happens in this here spot,"
O'Malley was complaining as he fell upon
the third quarter of pie. "And this mess has
no idea of a proper pie. They have nothing
but berry pie, which is little in the way of
pie."

"We'll be back on night flights up the
glory trail by tomorrow night, O'Malley,"
Allison said. "But right now the O.C. wants
to talk to the three of us in his office."

O'Malley gathered up the rest of the pie.
Allison scowled.

"I say, Irisher, you can't go in on the O.C.
with a platter of pie in your hand."

"Sure, and that's a fact," O'Malley
agreed. "Hold onto yerselves, boys, and
I'll fix it according to regulations." He
shoved half the piece of pie into his mouth.

Allison and Stan waited until he had finished. Then the three of them headed for
the O.C.'s office. Their rap at the door was

answered by a gruff voice and they entered.

The O.C. was a grizzled veteran of World War I. He looked at them with grim satisfaction. They were three of the best men he had, flying fools, ready to tackle any assignment.

"Sit down, gentlemen," he said gruffly.

They sat down, O'Malley slumping into his chair with his head thrust forward. He looked lank and hungry as he sat there and anyone except Stan and Allison would have said he hadn't had a square meal in a week.

The O.C. picked up a sheet of paper and stared at it, then he glowered at the three fliers. He cleared his throat and tapped the sheet of paper. His eyes were upon O'Malley. Suddenly he put the paper down.

"Something reminds me I have not had a bite to eat so far today," he said. "Do you boys mind if I have something sent in while I'm talking with you? I won't be able to get away later."

"Certainly not, sir," Allison said.

The O.C. was still looking at O'Malley. "Will you boys join me? A spot of tea or something?"

Before Allison or Stan could politely refuse, O'Malley answered, "Well, sir, I'm not partial to tea, but I could manage with a wee slab o' pie."

Allison glared at him while Stan struggled to smother a grin. The O.C. looked at them. "Would you boys have some pie?"

"No, thanks," both spoke in unison.

The O.C. rang and an orderly appeared. He took the Commander's order and hurried away. When the door closed the O.C. turned to Allison.

"I always get the bad part of every deal. Before me I have an order transferring you three men to Croydon Field. As soon as I get a few satisfactory men around me they are taken away." He looked sourly at O'Malley as though blaming him. "Take this wild man, O'Malley. He has begun to attract notice."

"It's been so quiet no man could attract notice," O'Malley said gloomily.

The O.C. smiled and fished another paper out of a tray. "Twenty-four hours in the air," he read. "Three Dornier bombers and two Messerschmitt fighters shot down by

Lieutenant O'Malley.'' He slid the report into a file. ''So this is quiet, eh?'' He actually smiled as he said it.

The orderly returned with a tray which O'Malley eyed hopefully. The O.C. lifted a cloth from his luncheon. The orderly carried a plate to O'Malley and handed him a fork. O'Malley waved the fork aside and scooped the pie off the plate. Sadly, he inspected it. It was blueberry, the same as his mess was supplying. Out of the side of his mouth he said:

''Ah well, it will do, but I thought it might be the O.C. ate at a different mess.''

''You boys will report to headquarters at Croydon at once.'' He looked at O'Malley and a startled expression came over his face. The Irisher's pie had disappeared.

''Yes, sir,'' Allison said and got to his feet.

The O.C. got to his feet and his wintry face cracked into a thin smile as he shook hands with each of the boys.

''This is quite a war and we have to hit as hard as we can and all pull together. They need you more at Croydon than I do here. Good luck to you.''

The three snapped salutes and faced about.

They hurried out of the building and across the square. Within a half-hour they were packed and ready for the car that was to take them to their new home.

"I'm not sorry saying good-by to those bloated balloons," Allison said as he looked up toward the south.

"I'm glad I'm leaving. It will save me punching a fellow officer in the jaw," Stan said grimly.

"There won't be anything excitin' goin' on over there," O'Malley said sourly.

"They may have some other kind of pie." Allison grinned.

An eager light came into O'Malley's eye. "Sure, and that's a thought worth remem-berin'," he muttered.

The mess at Croydon was a large room and had a phonograph as well as a console radio. There was a nice assortment of old but com-fortable chairs and lounges, and there was a counter where food and drinks were served. The three members of Red Flight arrived at the mess about the same time.

O'Malley saw the counter at once and his eyes lighted eagerly. Back of the counter were shelves and on one of the shelves sat a half-dozen pies. A Wing Commander and a Squadron Leader were leaning against the center of the counter. Allison was for barging on past without disturbing the superior officers, but O'Malley had his eyes on the pie shelf.

"Shove in, me hearties, the treat's on Mrs. O'Malley's son."

O'Malley shoved in beside the Wing Commander with Stan and Allison facing him.

"Tea," Allison ordered.

"Coffee, black," Stan said.

"Pie." O'Malley said it hungerly.

The corporal behind the pie counter fixed Allison's pot of tea and poured Stan's coffee, then he turned to O'Malley.

"What kind of pie, sir?"

For a moment O'Malley was struck dumb over his great good luck. This mess had a choice of pie.

"Apple," he said hopefully.

The corporal set a brown crusted pie on the counter and poised a knife over it. O'Malley reached over and took the knife. He proceeded to cut the pie four ways.

"But I say, sir, we don't cut pies that way.

It's against regulations, sir." The corporal was plainly flustered.

"Indaid?" O'Malley said. "An' could ye put down the whole pie in me chit book?"

"Of course, sir, but really if you let me cut it, sir, it wouldn't be ruined and you'll pay for only the portion you eat."

"Ah," O'Malley said and slid a quarter of the pie out of the tin and into his big hand. The corporal watched with fascination as the slab disappeared.

The Wing Commander was talking and the three junior officers could not avoid overhearing him.

"The Messerschmitt One-Tens coming over lately have a new gun. We'd like to get our hands on one of them, but so far we haven't salvaged anything."

"How about Intelligence in France? They ought to be able to get us something," said the Squadron Leader.

"No, if we get one it will be by pure accident," the Wing Commander answered sourly.

O'Malley was starting on his third piece

of pie. He had it in his hand and halfway to his open mouth. He lowered it and swung around to face the Wing Commander.

"The aisiest thing in the world, gettin' one of them guns," he said.

The Wing Commander turned toward O'Malley and looked from his face to the big slab of pie and then back again. His manner dripped frost. Allison got a glimpse of his insignia and kicked O'Malley on the shin. O'Malley grinned at the Wing Commander, then took a big bite of pie. The Wing Commander stiffened and snorted like a Merlin backfiring on a sub-zero morning.

"Did you speak, sir?" he asked.

O'Malley was unabashed, even when the Wing Commander bent a frigid look upon the wreck of the apple pie on the plate at his elbow.

"I said it would be aisy, gettin' one of them new guns," O'Malley repeated.

"Perhaps you can bring one to my office not later than tomorrow night," the Wing Commander snapped.

"And may I ask who I'll deliver it to?" O'Malley opened his mouth and the rest of the pie disappeared into it.

Signs of apoplexy began to show on the Wing Commander's face, but his voice was steady.

"Just deliver it to Wing Commander Farrell."

"Sure, an' I'll hand it to ye personal," O'Malley promised.

The Wing Commander bowed stiffly and turned away. The Squadron Leader wiped a smile off his lips and stared stonily at O'Malley. They marched off together.

"Now you've done it, you Irisher," Allison growled. "That's the man we have to fly under and I have to report to him within a half-hour."

" 'Tis a lot too many brass hats this man's army has around and I don't like them, but I'll do this Wing Commander a favor, bein' as he seemed a bit worked up over that new Jerry gun." O'Malley looked at the pie counter but shook his head. Five pies in one afternoon might spoil his dinner and he planned to enjoy a real feed.

Allison shoved off to report to the O.C. while Stan and O'Malley went over to the phonograph and turned it on. O'Malley lay on a divan with his feet well above his head.

Stan sat back in a deep chair. Before dozing off he wanted to ask the Irisher a question.

"Whatever made you pull that crack to the Wing Commander?"

"Sure, an' I was just offerin' to do me bit of winnin' the war," O'Malley said and closed his eyes.

Stan stared at him. It suddenly dawned upon him that O'Malley hadn't been fooling, he meant to deliver a Messerschmitt One-Ten to Wing Commander Farrell. He began to laugh. O'Malley opened his eyes and a grieved expression came over his face.

"You laughin' at me?" he demanded and there was a dangerous glint in his dark eyes.

"No," Stan said slowly. "I was thinking about how Wing Commander Farrell will look when you plump that gun down on his desk."

O'Malley grinned and closed his eyes again. "I'll let you go along with me," he said.

Stan studied the wild Irishman. He knew enough about O'Malley to expect anything from him. There could be no doubt but that Red Flight was in for some real circus stuff the next day. He hoped they contacted a flight of Messerschmitt One-Tens over the channel. He had no relish for the idea of trailing O'Malley into Germany and covering him while he filched a gun from one of Hitler's arsenals, but he was anxious to find out what scheme the Irisher had up his sleeve.

Allison came back and plumped into a chair. "I was lucky. The Wing Commander never suspected that I was with this wild Irishman. He thinks our hungry friend here is a ground man escaped from a nuthouse."

O'Malley made no comeback. He was sound asleep, his Adam's apple riding up and down gently, his lips moving as he snored deeply. Stan said in a low voice:

"He meant it when he offered to get a gun for the O.C."

"Now, now, you Yanks are gullible, everyone knows that, old man, but you shouldn't be taken in so easy."

"You wait and see," Stan said. "We'll have to stick with him no matter what fool stunt he pulls."

"Sure, old chap," Allison agreed, but the sardonic twist of his mouth showed he thought Stan as crazy as O'Malley. He got to his feet. "Don't let him miss dinner or we'll have trouble. We aren't on the call list until tomorrow morning. I have a bid to a bit of a dinner outside tonight."

"Gal?" Stan asked.

"Gal," Allison agreed.

"I'll wake the Irisher up," Stan promised.

The next morning Allison came barging into the breakfast room glowering savagely. He dropped into a chair across from Stan and O'Malley and snapped his order at the corporal. O'Malley gave him a brief look, then returned to his job of spreading jam on a huge stack of hot cakes which were flanked by a double order of sausages. The lank Irisher was not in a talkative mood. Stan grinned at Allison.

"What's eating on you? Did some civilian steal your gal?"

Allison glared at him. "We have friends over here at Croydon. The way they run a war! You'd think somebody would wake up to a few things!"

"What sort of an assignment did we get?" Stan was sure Allison was riled over the assignment they had been given.

"Nursing a flock of coal barges through the channel. Just big, lumbering boats not worth as much as the coal inside them. The Jerries won't waste a pound of T.N.T. on any of them. The only chance we'll have will be if they try to dive bomb a destroyer tagging along." Allison jerked a plate of bacon and eggs to him and shot a hard look at the corporal. "Black coffee," he snapped.

"We rate better than that," Stan said.

"My dear fellow," Allison spoke with elaborate politeness. "We have a friend over in the flight office. He got himself transferred yesterday so as to be helpful to us."

"He couldn't be anyone I know," Stan said.

"But of course he is. He is a dear friend of yours. In fact you offered to punch his nose for him once."

"Not Garret?" Stan stared at Allison.

"Lieutenant Arch Garret."

"How did he do it with a blackball against him?" Stan demanded.

"Pull, my dear fellow, as the Americans say. A drag somewhere. Now he's sitting where he can retire Red Flight to a peaceful life, and if we do bag a bandit, we'll have to have an affidavit from the King to get credit for it."

"How about a transfer?"

"No go, he'd have a finger in that too. In fact, my dear fellow, I applied for a transfer and got turned down, all before breakfast."

Stan looked across at O'Malley who was on his last hot cake. He was beaming pleasantly, his eyes looking out across the room. He had paid no attention at all to the bad news.

"You seem to like it, O'Malley," Allison growled.

"Huh?" the Irisher said with a start. Then he grinned. " 'Tis a poor spot in the channel that has no Messerschmitt One-Tens poking about in the clouds."

"And we'll sit around warming a chair waiting for a chance at a single or a double," Allison snapped.

"Sure, an' I can't be worried this mornin'," O'Malley said and got to his feet.

"What's got into him?" Allison asked sourly.

"You wouldn't believe it if I told you," Stan said with a wide grin.

Allison glared at him, and muttered, "You two make me tired."

CHAPTER V

O'MALLEY BAGS A JERRY GUN

No CALL came for Red Flight until late afternoon. Other flights roared away to strafe the French coast, or to meet incoming bomber formations, or to do scout duty; but Allison and his crew just sat around and groused. O'Malley's good humor finally broke down and he began prowling around hurling choice Irish words at the mess crew.

When the call did come, he was out of the room like a wild bushman. By the time Allison and Stan reached the cab rank, he was jerking his hatch cover into place and feeling out his Merlin.

"You'd think the boy was off to raid Berlin," Allison said sourly. "All we have is a call from a few barges of coal."

Red Flight roared out and up, heading toward the channel. Stan had checked his instruments carefully. Everything seemed

to be in working order, though he could not
be sure of his wing guns until he opened
them up.

"Keep in close," Allison's voice droned.

They were up now and heading for the
channel where a few big clouds hung over
the sea. So far as Stan could see they were
kings of the air and there might have been no
war on at all. Not a wing was in sight except their own.

"Red Flight, level off."

They leveled off and headed for a big
cloud. That seemed the most likely hunting
ground. The three Spitfires were not up
high because the clouds were hanging over
the sea. Below, Stan saw the cause of their
call. Seven of the foulest old tubs he had
ever laid an eye on were churning and wallowing in the choppy sea. Their propellers
thrashed the water into tawny foam. Their
plates were scarred and patched with daubs
of vermillion. Red, rusty streams of water
trickled down their sides. Seven piles of
rust, grime and junk belching smoke like so
many volcanoes. Coasters and not one of
them over twelve hundred tons.

The boats rode high and Stan decided they

were making the run from Portsmouth to London under ballast to pick up coal. Running what was supposed to be a death channel the old tubs would slide under the big coastal guns of the Germans. In a few days they would plough back loaded with coal. Their audacity made Stan grin. The British were certainly a stubborn race of people and when they had a sea course marked out they stayed with it. A sleek gray destroyer nosed the string of ancient boats along like a nervous hound herding a flock of fat pigs.

"Two bandits coming out of a cloud, quarter right," Allison's drawl announced.

Stan spotted the two Heinkel bombers as soon as Allison spoke. They were slim-bodied, snaky-looking killers with long wings and widespread tail structures. Their pilots hadn't seen the three Spitfires as yet, being busy spotting the sleek destroyer.

When they did see the danger they zoomed up and laid over, plunging back into the cloud. Stan drove straight after them because he was in the best position. O'Malley swept around one side of the cloud and Allison went around the other.

Stan had a chance to test his guns as his

upward zoom rode him up on a ghostly form
ahead in the mist. The eight Brownings
drilled furiously, in perfect timing. The
Heinkel nosed down and vanished into the
wall of fog. Stan went down to see if he had
done any damage.

Breaking into the clear he saw blossoms of
white silk dotting the green of the sea. The
bombers were gone but Stan knew from the
number of chutes floating down to the water
that both Heinkels had been bagged.

Below them two motor launches were slicing across the channel getting set to pick up
the Jerries and make them prisoners. Then
he heard O'Malley's voice.

"Sure, an' I'm thinkin' I see four Messers off the port wing."

"Coming up with you," Allison called
back. "Take them, Irisher."

"Wilson coming up," Stan shouted into
his flap mike.

He went up and over a cloud and down on
the other side. He saw O'Malley drilling
away to the south like an irate bumblebee.
Close behind him streaked Allison. Stan
headed after them. Then Allison's voice
came in very softly:

"I think you're seeing things, Irisher."

Stan grinned as he shoved the nose of the Spitfire down a little. O'Malley was duck hunting. He didn't aim to go back without some more action if he could help it.

"Red Flight, come in. Red Flight, come in," droned a voice from the field.

"Red Flight in contact with bandits!" O'Malley roared back.

"Red Flight, come in. Red Flight, come in," headquarters insisted.

"Red Flight going into defense," Allison cut in.

Stan's grin widened. Allison was going to see that O'Malley got his duck hunt. They roared on, swinging in a wide circle, beating upward again. O'Malley would have his way now. Allison couldn't argue with headquarters listening in.

Stan began to think they were stymied when all Hades broke loose from above. Out of nowhere five Messerschmitts came roaring down on them, three One-Nines and two One-Tens.

"Prepare for attack. Peel off and take some altitude," Allison drawled.

"Start peelin', darlin'," Bill O'Malley shouted.

They zoomed upward, spreading to let the attack slide past. The enemy scattered out and swooped to meet them. Stan saw O'Malley drive straight over a One-Nine almost ramming the Jerry, and missing him clean with a burst of fire. That was not like O'Malley.

The Jerry banked and flipped over, thinking only of getting away before O'Malley cut back across him and sawed him in two parts; but O'Malley kept straight on. Stan picked up the One-Nine, scissoring off a wing tip and sending him wavering away toward the east.

Stan watched O'Malley as the wild Irishman zoomed up over a One-Ten. The Messerschmitt banked and tried to escape, but O'Malley was on him in a reckless roaring dive. Stan shot over the two and saw the Jerry spray O'Malley's ship with lead. Pieces of his hatch cover showered away like feathers from a potted duck. Again O'Malley missed a perfect burst and came up under the Jerry. He returned the compliment

paid him by slicing the top off the Messerschmitt's hatch cover. Stan knew the miss
had been deliberate. O'Malley never let one
get away when he had a spot shot like that.

Then light dawned upon Stan. O'Malley
was after the Jerry's gun. Allison was very
busy himself and doing such a savage job
that he was about to clear the air without
Stan's help. Stan dived down to make the
game one against one for Allison. When he
came up, O'Malley was on the tail of the
Messerschmitt and bawling at Allison:

"By the shades of St. Patrick, you keep
out of this!"

The Jerry was hurt, but not badly, and
O'Malley had him on the run. When the
Jerry dived O'Malley was on his tail. He
didn't shoot him down. When he dropped
off on one wing, peeling away under full
throttle, O'Malley had him covered. Then
Stan heard the Irisher yelling at the Jerry
pilot.

"Leave that gun like she is, you spalpeen,
or I'll send you to the fishes!"

Apparently the Jerry did not understand
what O'Malley said, possibly his radio

wasn't set to pick up the transmitter of the
Spitfire, but he did understand the short
bursts of fire that clipped pieces out of various parts of his ship. He headed the way the
lank Irishman pointed and drove ahead.

Allison and Stan dropped in behind, letting O'Malley have his prize. Stan called to
Allison:

"Somebody ought to tip off the Ack-Ack
boys or O'Malley may get a warm reception."

"Let him show his stuff," Allison drawled
and Stan thought he heard the Flight Lieutenant chuckle.

The Messerschmitt ducked over the coast
and down with O'Malley steering him ex-
pertly to the field. Bursts of gunfire began
to blossom below and puffs of white smoke
broke around the Jerry and his pursuer.

"They think O'Malley's Spitfire is a captured plane with a Jerry in it," Stan muttered.

O'Malley sent his catch down through the
shellfire, twisting and turning. The Nazi
pilot was an expert and wiggled through until they got close in, then the fire got so hot he

and O'Malley had to hit for the ceiling. They circled and were high up when Stan and Allison slid down the field.

Undaunted, O'Malley came in again and this time he sent his prize through the rain of exploding shells. The Messerschmitt rolled to a stop with O'Malley close behind him. In a moment the flustered Jerry was climbing out of his shattered hatch with his hands elevated above his head.

Ground men closed in around him, shouting and doing a war dance. O'Malley climbed out after removing part of the hatch cover from around his neck. He strode to the Messerschmitt and bellowed at the ground men.

"Git ye a hump on yerselves an' pull out that fore gun!"

Four mechanics raced away to get tools while O'Malley stood guard over his prize. He refused to let anyone touch the ship. A senior ground officer came hurrying up and O'Malley gave him a sloppy salute. The offcer snapped:

"I'll take charge here now."

"Ye'll do nothing of the sort," O'Malley

shouted. "And as I live and breathe them's Wing Commander Farrell's very orders!"

The officer looked at the wild-eyed O'Malley and decided it would be best to wait for reinforcements, possibly a Group Captain or an Air Commodore.

"It's my job, you know, old man," he said but his tone had changed.

" 'Tis my job, me hearty," O'Malley assured him.

The mechanics arrived and in a few minutes the fore gun was on the ground at O'Malley's feet. It was so heavy he could not handle it. He turned to the grinning Stan who was standing beside Allison.

"Lend a hand so we can deliver this gadget before sundown."

Stan and Allison stepped forward.

"This is positively against regulations," the senior officer sputtered.

"An' who, may I ask, bagged this here gun?" O'Malley demanded. "I may be bold, but I suggest ye give some attention to that Jerry waitin' over there to be captured accordin' to regulations."

The Jerry was standing with his arms still

elevated. He was alone and unguarded.

"And be lettin' O'Malley of Red Flight be knowin' where you put the bye. I aim to see that he has cigarettes and a few of the common comforts." O'Malley grinned at the Jerry. The youngster grinned back at him and saluted stiffly.

Dragging the gun between them, the three members of Red Flight stamped across the field and barged past a startled sentry who was walking post outside headquarters.

Wing Commander Farrell was just finishing a flight report. His gray eyes were hard and his mouth was drawn into a tight line. Coral Raid had dropped two bombers and three fighters. The credit side showed only one fighter and a Junkers. Farrell looked up and his eyes rested upon a lank and hungry-looking Irish youth. He stared at O'Malley for a long minute, then remembered him and his pie.

"What do you want, Lieutenant?" he snapped. "I suppose you have that new enemy gun in your pocket."

His sarcasm was lost upon O'Malley. He grinned wolfishly as he stepped aside.

"Indaid, an' I hope it's the latest model.

I put a very good Jerry flier to a lot of trouble to be after fetchin' it to you.''

The Wing Commander's eyes popped out as he stared at the machine Allison and Stan had dropped upon the floor. Suddenly he leaped out of his chair and charged around the desk. Getting down on his knees, he bent over the gun and examined it. When he straightened he was smiling.

"So you are the wild Irishman we have been hearing about," he said. "It would seem some rumors are correct in this war."

"An' now, sor, I'll be running along," O'Malley said. "I'm feelin' a bit o' the pinch of hunger."

"Have two pies on my chit book," the Wing Commander said and smiled broadly.

"Indaid, that I will," O'Malley answered gravely.

The three coal barge nurses returned to the briefing room and checked their chutes which had been discarded on the field. They found Lieutenant Garret waiting for them. He drew his mouth into a triumphant frown. Beside his desk lay the three chutes, neatly piled there by the field crew.

"See those chutes?" he snapped.

"Sure, an' one of them gadgets is a personal friend o' mine," O'Malley said and grinned broadly.

"I'm putting it down against you. You discarded them on the field without properly caring for them. That is a violation of general orders." Garret scowled at the Irish flier.

O'Malley leaned his elbows on the desk and regarded the officer thoughtfully.

"Very remarkable, indaid," he said softly.

"Red Flight reports two Dorniers and three Messerschmitts down and one captured," Allison said and his eyes locked with those of the briefing officer.

"Red Flight gets credit for two Dorniers. The Royal Navy reported them. And one Messerschmitt brought in." Garret's eyes gleamed triumphantly.

"Sure, an' are ye certain ye can give us one Messer?" O'Malley asked. "Perhaps the poor bye got himself lost an' mistook this berg for Berlin."

"There is no independent check on the other fighters," Garret snapped.

Stan said nothing. He could not trust himself to speak. What he wanted to do was to lay a right on Garret's jaw.

"You fellows better walk pretty straight from now on. And keep yourself looking like officers," Garret barked.

Without bothering to fill in a report, O'Malley shoved off to the mess room. Allison filled out his report and Stan made his out. They reported the exact action and the results. They left Garret scowling at their cards.

"Wilson!" Garret called sharply as Stan started to walk away at Allison's side. "I want a word with you, alone."

Stan turned back and stood at the desk. His gaze locked with Garret's.

"Have you ever flown stunts or test jobs in the United States?" He leaned forward and his small eyes searched Stan's face.

Stan returned his stare. "You have my card where you can dig it out. Suppose you take a look at it?" Stan turned on his heel and walked away.

Garret let him go without asking any more questions, but he was shaking his head and frowning as though trying to remember something or somebody that had slipped his mind.

"He's about got my number," Stan muttered to himself as he went into the mess.

CHAPTER VI

THE SEA DOGS GROWL

STAN stepped out of the barracks and stood for a moment watching the scene on the field before the hangars. A row of Defiants had been rolled out. Men worked around them or scurried to and from the hangars. There was an uneasy feel about the scene. Stan scented action and a feeling of irritation filled him. Red Flight was on barge patrol when it should have been on combat. It was fools like Garret who messed up battle plans.

He was about to turn toward the mess division and had turned into the narrow alley leading to the building, when he halted and stepped back, close to the wall. Garret was coming out of the doorway of the mess and beside him walked a tall man. The man had a lean, weathered face with a scar across the right cheek. He wore a checked suit and a pearl-gray hat with a broad brim. The hat could have come from no place but the western part of the United States.

Stan recognized him at once as Charles L. Milton. He didn't have to guess twice why Garret had him in hand and why he had taken him to the squadron mess. Garret wanted Milton to see Stan. Quickly moving around a corner, Stan headed for a hangar. He was sure they had not seen him.

As he strode swiftly along, Stan faced the ghost of his past. Milton was an American aircraft engineer. He had designed at least two of the newest models and knew everyone in the industry over in the United States. He knew Stan Wilson very well. As he entered the hangar Stan reflected bitterly that he should have known the British Isles would be swarming with American experts and engineers, now that a great effort was being made to help the besieged English nation. He had about as much chance of hiding in a Royal Air Force squadron as Joe Louis would have in not being recognized at Madison Square Garden.

He might be able to dodge Milton for a while. If he could only shake Garret he might do it for quite a while. Not that his conscience wasn't clear. He had been framed. Framed by Nazi saboteurs, Fifth Column operators. That was the reason he was so eager to get in every lick he could against the monster Hitler had built to swallow the world.

He stood inside the shaded doorway to the hangar and watched Milton step into a car. When the car had rolled away he turned back toward headquarters. Within an hour he had to be back where he could hear the blare of the intersquadron speaker, to be on call for duty. He was moving along, scowling at the busy scene upon the field. As he passed the door of the O.C.'s office it opened and Wing Commander Farrell stepped out. Stan saluted and the commander returned the salute. He halted abruptly.

"Well, well," he said. "Just the man I'm looking for. Come in, Lieutenant."

Stan's heart dropped with a thud. This likely meant a lot of questions to be answered, questions put into the O.C.'s head by Garret.

"Yes, sir," he answered and followed the Commander inside.

Farrell seated himself behind his desk. He motioned toward a chair. "Sit down, Wilson."

Stan sat down and waited. The Commander fished into his desk and took out a cigar. He clipped the end off with a silver knife, then lighted the weed and looked at Stan.

"Allison tells me you have had a lot of experience with various types of fast planes. Testing over in Canada. Most of the American ships have been going through trials up there. Did you have a chance at any of them?"

Stan breathed more freely. "Yes, sir," he said.

"We have a new type American plane here." The Commander fished through some papers, found a blue sheet and studied it for a minute. "They call this one the Hendee Hawk. We have tested it and found it to be rather fast but very tricky." The Commander frowned at the report, then looked up at Stan.

Stan could hardly hold back a grin and a whoop. Did he know the Hendee Hawk? He knew the Hawk from her prop to her tail assembly. The Wing Commander was

being very conservative when he said the
Hawk was rather fast. Stan had squinted
at her air-speed indicator when it was jig-
gling crazily at 600 miles per hour. He
waited for the Wing Commander to go on.

"Ordinarily we would train enough special men to handle these ships, but we are
pressed for fighting ships at the moment."

Stan's face did not reveal anything of
what he was thinking. The Britisher was
talking calmly and appeared not to be worried. Stan knew the need for Hendee
Hawks was desperate, and he knew the ships
would deliver.

"Have you many of them, sir?" he asked.

"No. This ship is a test job." The Wing
Commander dropped the blue sheet. "Have
you ever flown a Hendee Hawk?"

"Yes, sir."

The question Stan expected to follow did
not come. Wing Commander Farrell said
nothing for more than a minute.

"Would you like to take this one? Into
action?"

Stan restrained a smothering eagerness.
He wanted to jump up and down and shout,
to slap the Commander on the back. A lot

of experts had turned thumbs down on the Hawk. But the saboteur boys had known she was the super-plane and had done everything they could to get her junked, including a nice frame-up on himself. He knew they had just about succeeded if there was only one ship here in Britain.

"I'll fly her, sir," he said and added eagerly, "she is the greatest combination of fighter and strafing plane ever built. She packs enough bombs to do real damage, as well."

The Wing Commander smiled. "We shall see," he said.

The way he said it convinced Stan it was up to him to show both the British and the Jerries just what the Hendee Hawk could do. If this ship failed, there would be no more of the machines he had worked so hard to help perfect.

"She carries two men," Stan said.

"I have been considering that." Suddenly the Wing Commander laughed outright. "Do you suppose your friend, the pie-eating Irishman, would care to work with you? I should like to have Allison become familiar with the ship, too. In that

way we would have three men able to in-
struct others if we order more of these
fighters.''

''I don't know,'' Stan said honestly.

''I could assign them to you, but I prefer
to let you ask them,'' Farrell said. Then he
got to his feet. ''You will report to 7-B at
once.''

Stan grinned broadly. It would take him
away from Garret, at least until the snooping Lieutenant was able to locate him again.
He saluted and hurried out of the office.

Stan actually sneaked into the mess. He
couldn't afford to have this chance smashed
by a cluck like Garret. The coast was clear.
Only a few fliers were lounging about, with
Allison and O'Malley among them. Stan
crossed the room and sat down between his
pals. He did not notice, in his excitement,
that they seemed to be expecting him. The
clock over the counter showed that in one
minute Allison and O'Malley would go on
duty. He wondered who would fill in for
him in Red Flight.

''Sure, an' you've been shunnin' us,''
O'Malley greeted him.

Stan came to the point at once. ''How

would you like to copilot a real ship, an American ship?" he asked, looking from one to the other.

"I'd prefer a glider," Allison said with a wicked leer.

"How about you, Irisher?"

"I wouldn't mind if me pal didn't hog the controls all the blessed time." O'Malley grinned.

"She's a stinger. You'll see something you never thought was in the bag. She's tricky as a Navaho Indian."

"Is that a Canadian tribe of wild men?" Allison drawled.

"Sure," Stan came back. "Hudson's Bay."

Allison snorted.

"I'm with you," O'Malley cut in. "Anything to get off this deadhead beat the muckle heads have us on. Mrs. O'Malley's boy came down to London to see some action."

"Good. I'll get in touch with the O.C. at once." Stan got to his feet.

"Really, old chap, you're not going to rush off without my final answer. I'm in on this if I have to fly a kite," Allison said with a wide smile.

Stan put on a cold expression. Allison hadn't fooled him. He had known the lank Britisher would come in. Allison had that look in his eye he always got when something was up.

"Thanks, Allison."

"You should thank me. I'm giving up a flight lieutenant's job."

"You'll still be leader and we'll demand the Red Flight label. We'll have three of the meanest brutes that ever rolled out on a line to make the other boys jealous." Stan slapped Allison on the back. "Let's go."

They reported to the Wing Commander, then shifted their things to B-7. Later they went over to the hangar to have a look at the Hawk. Allison said very little, but O'Malley was as tickled as a kid with a new top. He went over everything and the only thing he crabbed about was the cramped quarters furnished for the copilot, who handled the bomb release and the extra guns.

They checked in at their new mess and Stan felt better. He looked in at the briefing room and found it presided over by a fat young man with a broad smile. In the mess he met no one he knew. Everything looked

fine and he settled down to watch O'Malley
devour a pie.

O'Malley finished his pie and looked hungerly across the room at the counter in the
corner. He shook his head sadly.

"If I eat one more me lunch will be spoilt
sure."

Stan grinned as he glanced at his wrist
watch. It lacked a half-hour until official
eating time.

After lunch they made further arrange-
ments for their new job. Allison was to fly
with them in a Spitfire. O'Malley went
along with Stan as a gunner and student,
with care of the bomb racks in his hands.
With everything set and ready to go, the re-
vised and rehashed Red Flight prepared to
take a little outing. Being on test work
gave them plenty of freedom to choose their
own jobs.

They slipped away without much notice
being taken of the new ship. Everyone was
busy with his own job and paid no attention
to the big fighter sliding out on its tricycle
landing gear with a Spitfire nosing right
after it.

Stan settled back to have some fun with

Allison. Out of the corner of his eyes he watched the vertical speed indicator and a wide grin spread over his face. The Hendee Hawk was going up at a terrific pace. Already the Spitfire was far behind. Stan knew Allison would fly the wings off the Spitfire to keep him from getting away. He laughed softly.

He kicked her over and into a tight bank and she zoomed around, boring away. He kicked her back and looped in a dizzy blur of speed. Allison shot in below him and Stan came around to knife past his pal. He glanced back and there was a happy, vacant grin on O'Malley's homely face, as he absorbed the drone of the 2,000-horsepower, two-row, radial motor.

Allison dipped his wings as Stan went boring past him. It was really a salute and it meant a lot, coming from Allison with his dislike of radial motors.

They roared out over the channel at 15,000 feet. As the French coast line began to show through a thin mist, Stan laid over and started to climb again. Very soon they were nipping at their oxygen, flying at 26,-000 feet. They saw no planes at all and the excursion seemed doomed to be no more than a spring frolic.

O'Malley growled into his intercommunication phone. "The Jerries must o' heard we were comin' out for a spin."

"There's a cloud or two down and to the east," Stan answered. "We'll drop down and pick up Allison, then go have a look."

"That's where the bushwhackin' spalpeens will be lurking," O'Malley agreed.

They knifed over on one wing, peeled off, and roared down. The gyro-horizon did a lot of strange maneuvers and the altimeter was unrolling like ticker tape off a Wall Street machine. They picked up Allison and Stan decided to give the Irishman a lesson. He set the air flaps, and before the startled O'Malley could save himself, he had lost a couple of inches of skin off both shins. The Hendee Hawk seemed to have decided to stop in mid-air. She was pointing her nose straight at the ground, but she had slowed to a steady 350 miles per hour.

"Mother o' pearl!" O'Malley shouted. "What a nice day for dive bombing. Show me how you do it."

"Just watch." Stan pulled the Hawk out

of her dive and then sent her in again with O'Malley watching him closely.

Then Allison's voice cut in. "You fellows better cut out the grandstanding and have a look west."

Stan looked and saw that Allison was streaking away toward a formation of nine Junkers Ju 87s. The Stukas were bent upon business and were moving toward the English coast, undoubtedly bent upon intercepting a ship they had received a spotter's report upon.

"Me bye, you may now show Mrs. O'Malley's son a few things," O'Malley bellowed. Stan sent the Hawk sizzling away after the Stukas. The Jerries had now sighted the two fighters, but they were keeping on their course, which meant that up in the big clouds above lurked a fighter patrol of Messerschmitts. The Junkers were slow and low-powered, not being able to exceed 170 miles per hour. Stan zoomed up and passed Allison who was also going up with the cloud ambush in mind.

Suddenly the Stukas broke formation and scattered, each diving for cover and cutting loose their sticks of bombs. Stan banked and selected a bomber as his victim. Through his windscreen he caught a glimpse of Allison and his hand stiffened on the control. A cloud of Jerry fighters had dropped out of the blue upon the Spitfire. Allison had gone wild as he always did. His Spitfire was a whirling, twisting demon, its eight wing guns flaming. But Allison hadn't a chance against that swarm of Jerries.

Stan shot upward to get into the play. He cut loose the bombs from his racks and gave the Hawk all she had. He had a wide space of blue to cut through and as he bored in he saw Allison's ship lay over in a wabbly, sickening lurch and then nose down.

"Guns out, motor stuttering. Have to go in," Allison's drawl came over the radio.

The Hendee Hawk roared into the whirling mass of Jerry fighters and its banks of guns roared. The Jerries slid away after they had tasted the terrible gun power of this new ship.

Stan nosed down and plummeted after Allison who had two Messerschmitts on his tail, but when the Hawk overtook them in one terrific spurt they swerved aside, each sending a final spray of lead over Allison's ship. Stan picked the one on the right and laid over to cut across the Messer with all his Brownings drilling. A wing sheared away from the Messer and shot up and out of sight. The Messerschmitt went rolling down.

Stan dived after Allison. He didn't like the way the Spitfire was wobbling and turning. He had once seen a ship come in that way and when the boys got to it the pilot was dead. All he could do was trail Allison who failed to answer his frantic calls.

The Spitfire kept going until she was almost to the field. As she slid out over the turf she wavered and her nose went down. She dived a few hundred feet, straightened, then slid off on one wing. Again she straightened and leveled out, close to the ground now. Suddenly she put her nose down and plunged to earth, landing with a smash that made her ground loop and pile up close to a hangar door.

Stan set the Hawk down and slid over to the wrecked Spitfire. He and O'Malley leaped out and ran to the ship. The ground men had dragged Allison out. He was slumped between two of them, his face bloodless, his lips tight with pain. The old, mocking flicker was in his eyes as he shoved aside the arms of the men and smiled at Stan.

"I take back everything I've said about Yank planes," he said, then he slid gently into Stan's arms, a limp rag of a man.

Stan gathered him up and carried him toward a field ambulance which was roaring toward them with its siren screaming, while O'Malley trudged along behind muttering savagely to himself.

A white-coated ambulance surgeon leaped out to meet them as the ambulance slithered to a stop. Stan laid his burden down gently and stepped back out of the way, dragging O'Malley with him. The surgeon knelt beside the unconscious man and made a swift examination, then turned and snapped to a couple of internes hovering behind him:

"Get a stretcher down here. This man is badly wounded."

Stan surged forward and clutched his arm. "How badly?" he queried through bloodless lips. "Not . . .?"

The surgeon smiled and placed a reassuring hand on his shoulder. "No," he replied simply. "I promise you he won't die. England needs all her fliers, and we'll pull him through to go into the air again. I can't tell how soon," he ended briskly. "Not until I get him to the hospital and make a complete examination." He turned away and leaped into the ambulance behind the stretcher, and it sped away with its unconscious burden.

"Glory be to God," breathed O'Malley fervently. "Come along with you now, we'd best make our reports."

In the briefing room the flight officer met them with more eagerness than was usual with such an official. Nodding toward the chutes, neatly piled on the floor, he said:

"You usually take care of those things, don't you know."

Stan nodded grimly. He was thinking about Allison. O'Malley just grunted and planked his bony elbows on the high desk. Thrusting his chin out, he remarked:

"What you limeys need is more fire wagons like I just slid meself out of. I want one for my own use."

"I heard the new ship was a bit of all right," the flight officer said. "I'll take your report. The Wing Commander wants it rushed right over."

"We'll be after blushin' to give you the actual facts of what happened," O'Malley said slowly.

"One Messerschmitt to us and three to Allison," Stan answered.

The officer nodded and began scribbling. "Fill out one for me right away." He shoved a blank across the desk.

"How about the varmint I dissected with me guns?" O'Malley asked.

"Did you hit one of those Stukas?" Stan asked.

"Sure, an' I did that," O'Malley said.

"One Stuka badly damaged," Stan added.

They went into the mess and for once O'Malley did not order a pie. He sat down and stared at the ceiling, his big mouth clamped shut, his Adam's apple sliding up and down. Finally he said:

"Next time I get to take her, I can fly her like she was me own wings."

"You might as well. This job is half yours," Stan said. "Until we find out about Allison this flight will have only two men and one ship."

"Allison's going to be right back with us. The bye wouldn't kick off until he had had a

chance to wind up this new colleen we got.''
O'Malley said it grimly, as though trying
to make himself believe.

"Here comes Wing Commander Farrell
and I think he's looking for us," Stan said.

"Sure, an' 'tis the big man himself and
no other. An' comin' to see us instead of
us tramping over there. Me bye, the first
thing we know, the King will be dropping in
to have a spot of tea with us two intrepid
fliers.'' O'Malley's big mouth was spread in
a wide grin.

"Don't get up, men," the Wing Commander said as he came up. He seated himself
and started in briskly. "I hear the Hawk
is better than anyone thought.''

"Not better than I thought," Stan said.

"Well, better than the inspectors and test
men thought. They said she wasn't relia-
ble.''

"She is sensitive and temperamental,"
Stan agreed.

"She chops up a Messerschmitt and spits
out the pieces like me auld granddaddy used
to whack up a box for kindlin'," O'Malley
broke in.

"Fine." The Wing Commander smiled

broadly. "I just dropped by to ask you boys to stay very close to quarters. We have reports of activity at sea and there may be quite a bit of action. I'd like to find out if this ship is really a dive bomber."

O'Malley grinned happily and saluted the Wing Commander. He had not taken the trouble to get to his feet. Farrell returned the salute without so much as the twitch of a facial muscle.

"We'll be ready, sir." Stan stood at attention.

The Wing Commander walked away and Stan scowled down at his pal. "A fine officer you are."

"Naval action, and my turn comin' up," O'Malley gloated.

An orderly called Stan to the telephone. When he returned he was smiling.

"Allison will make it. He won't be laid up very long."

"Hooray!" O'Malley shouted and leaped into the air. He headed straight across the room toward the counter. The corporal saw him coming and slid an apple pie off the shelf.

CHAPTER VII

THE Wing Commander seemed bent upon saving the Hendee Hawk for some special show. For two days no call came for Stan and O'Malley. They lounged about, with O'Malley getting as restless as a panther and twice as grouchy. They went over to see Allison and found him sitting up. He would be out in a very short time.

Stan took the opportunity to give O'Malley a course of lessons dealing with the fine points of the Hawk.

"She carries two sticks of bombs when she's out hunting. That's something new. They put those sticks on just to pep you up. The other day, when we were zipping through Messerschmitt bullets, I gave them a thought or two. If a cannon ball or a bullet lands just right, off goes the stick of bombs and out you go." Stan grinned at O'Malley as he spoke.

111

"Sure, an' O'Malley will fix that," the Irishman said. "We pick a nice spot and drop them firecrackers."

"I'm glad you suggested it. It would have been against regulations for me to say anything about it."

"Sure, we might find a Jerry to pop them down on, but no matter, they are no fit things to be kapin' tucked under your wings whilst you're sky scrappin'." O'Malley shook his head.

"We'll try them out. This is the best dive bomber that was ever built. You nose her straight down and pull the flaps. She settles herself to a 350 mile per hour pace and when you get your sights set you cut loose. It's a dead cinch to pot a target that way."

"Sure," O'Malley agreed. "Only we aren't bomber boys."

They left O'Malley's room and went to the mess. Stan read the pictorial while O'Malley took a nap. The blaring of the intersquadron speaker roused them. The Irishman's feet hit the floor and he was awake at once.

"That's us," he mumbled.

"It's everybody else, but it's not us," Stan growled.

It seemed the Group Captain and his men gathered around the map in headquarters had forgotten all about the Hendee Hawk.

"That's the trouble in being a one-ship flight," O'Malley muttered. "If we had three Spitfires we'd be up there now."

An orderly entered and ran across to Stan. "Wing Commander Farrell's instructions for Lieutenant Wilson," he said as he handed Stan the paper.

Stan unfolded the paper and, with O'Malley reading the order out loud over his shoulder, he scanned the paper. They were to join a flight of Hurricanes and Spitfires setting out to contact enemy planes over the channel. Orders would be broadcast later, but the action was in connection with a naval attack. Their radio call would be Red Flight.

"Sure, an' we're still Red Flight," O'Malley said as he whirled and made off.

They walked back to O'Malley's room. Over a battered desk hung a piece of the tail of a Dornier showing a swastika and on the desk lay a heavy German pistol, a grim memento of some duel with death he had won.

Surveying these enemy souvenirs, Stan grinned broadly and remarked, "If this war keeps up you'll be able to furnish a museum."

O'Malley shook his head disconsolately. " 'Tis little enough," he complained. "This air fighting is bad for picking up such things. Every time I down a plane it's me bad luck that it smashes to bits and leaves nothing behind for me to remember it by."

"The ones that smash up feel worse about it than you do," Stan reminded him.

The Irishman turned serious for one of the few times since Stan had known him. "Faith, an' I think of them poor devils sometimes," he muttered. " 'Tis hard for them with nothing to believe in. Fighting because they're told to fight. Crashing to flaming death because one man orders them to. 'Tis a bad state of affairs this world is in, so help me."

Stan nodded soberly. "The best we can do is to finish the whole show up as fast as

we can. And we'd better be getting back
to the mess to be ready for a call."

O'Malley yawned and nodded agreement.
"Though it's not likely they'll be sending us
up again soon," he muttered pessimistically.
"Always coddlin' us, that's what they do."

A few minutes later they were waddling
out on the field. The blast of steel propellers
sawed through the air as a Spitfire flight
warmed up on the cab rank. Cantilever
wings vibrated and hummed and figures in
coveralls swarmed over and around the
planes. Flight sergeants tested throttle
knobs and officers dashed about.

"Looks like an extra big show," Stan said
as they moved toward the newly daubed
hawk. She looked freakish in her many-
colored coat of sky paint. Her motor was
idling smoothly.

"Sure, an' she's a dainty colleen," O'Malley purred as he waited for the sergeant to
swing down.

"Remember this ship has to come back,
so don't go wild," Stan warned. "And let
me have her when we get ready to unload
those sticks of T.N.T. If we crack her up

and no record comes in, we won't get any more Hawks. The brass hats over here aren't sold on her yet."

O'Malley was dreamily grinning at the big fighter and didn't seem to hear him.

The Sergeant swung down and flipped a salute. "That motor is a bit of all right, sir," he said.

"She is that," Stan agreed.

They climbed in and got set in their cramped quarters. Seated very close together, with Stan a bit lower than O'Malley, who was at the controls, they pulled up their belts. O'Malley jerked his hatch cover shut and Stan closed his. The Irishman revved up, pinched one brake and gave the throttle a kick. The Hawk spun around with a roar. Stan noted the look of surprise on the Irishman's face. He hoped O'Malley didn't ground loop her before they got off.

O'Malley didn't. He was a born flier and a lover of engines. Before they got the starter's signal, he had the feel of the big Double-Wasp motor. He took her off with a rush and a zoom, falling easily into place between a flight of Spitfires and Hurricanes. Later a spread of Defiants joined them and

still later they overtook a squadron of
Hampdens moving steadily out toward the
channel. The bombers were loaded heavily
and making no attempt to climb up.

"Don't ye forget we're pickin' a target
and unloading the bombs." O'Malley was
speaking through the "intercom" telephone.

"Wait until we spot a good target. I
want to see what we can do with our sticks
of bombs," Stan answered.

O'Malley began to hum a snatch of an
Irish melody. He wasn't in the least dis-
turbed. For that matter the whole flight
was slipping along as smoothly as though
on parade.

Then everything changed in a flash.
"Naval battle! Naval battle!" O'Malley
was bellowing into his mike.

The Hampdens were moving into formation for action against something below and
the fighters were peeling off and going down
to see them through. Up ahead shells were
bursting in the sky and the thunder of big
guns rolled up to them.

"Boom! Boom! Boom!"

The big fellows weren't tossing their shells

aloft. They were lobbing them at targets below. Stan shouted to O'Malley:

"Follow the Hampdens down so we can unload!"

"Sure, an' the quicker the better," O'Malley bellowed back. He depressed the nose of the Hawk and they went screaming down the chute. In a moment they had a good look at the sea below.

Four cruisers and a string of light destroyers were fighting a running battle with several pocket battleships and a fleet of coastal torpedo boats. An aircraft carrier wallowed alongside the formation of cruisers.

The scene below was a wild mixture of foaming water, smoke and flame from belching guns, and the roll of thunder as the turret batteries fired. The British Navy dogs were trying to get at the pocket battleships. The carrier held her course well west of the line of destroyers. The cruisers were pouring broadsides across the lashed water, and the destroyers, like bull pups, were pounding away, holding station splendidly, trying to reach the enemy. One got a hit squarely on its foredeck and rolled half around, wallowing in the trough. A sheet of flame spurted from a gun turret and rolled over the deck. For a moment the little ship staggered on, then exploded.

"The poor fellers," grated O'Malley.

Stan said nothing but he felt cold all over. He looked down at the carrier and saw torpedo bombers sliding off her deck like little swallows. O'Malley's voice chopped off his thoughts.

" 'Tis a pocket battle wagon we get, no less," he almost crooned.

"Thick weather down there," Stan warned.

The muck of anti-aircraft fire made the stratum above the sea look as though it was on fire. The smoke was stabbed by blossoming shells hurling ragged pieces of iron in every direction. There was a swarm of Messerschmitts and Stukas and Heinkels all messed up with a crisscross of darting, thrusting Hurricanes, Spitfires and Defiants. The Hampdens were not having any better luck in getting through to their objectives than were the Stukas.

"We better set the firecrackers off or we'll miss one foin scrap," O'Malley called.

He nosed the Hawk down and sent her into a screaming dive. The little boats that Stan knew were pocket battleships began to grow in size, and the muck swarmed up closer to them with Hades breaking loose around their ears. None of the Messerschmitts tried to stop them. The Jerries thought the odd plane was just another crazy fighter who didn't know where he was going. The cockpit shuddered and the instruments on the board seemed to dance.

"Set your wing flaps!" Stan screamed. "Set your flaps!"

The Hawk began to steady as O'Malley remembered the flaps and applied them. Holding a plumb line at 350 miles per hour, she dropped upon the battle wagon below. Stan could see the deck of the ship coming up toward them as though a mighty hand were lifting it.

The wind screamed above the din of exploding shells. The gunners on board the battleship were taking notice and frantically trying to swing guns to bear upon the plummeting Hawk. Stan caught his breath and held it. This was exhilarating, almost glorious. He didn't think about the danger of meeting a bursting shell, all he thought about was the drop and the mighty surge of power. The plane swayed and shuddered as big shells burst close to her.

Then the field of blossoming shells was above them and the deck below was big. They could see men scrambling about, their faces white blobs as they looked upward.

"Left a point," Stan shouted as he set the bomb sight. "Now right a bit . . . left more."

"Ready!" O'Malley bellowed.

"Ready! Hold her steady!"

O'Malley released the bomb selection levers, both of them.

All Stan had to do was to press the button and the sticks of bombs were off. He pressed it hard and almost instantly the ship zoomed upward as though tossed into the sky by a mortar. As they wound upward with the Wasp engine roaring Stan looked back.

Where the deck of the battleship had been there was now a great burst of smoke and flame.

"That card will make 'em watch their course, me bye!" O'Malley crowed.

Stan could not tell whether they had put the pocket battleship out or not. She shifted her course and moved more slowly, but she kept going. Now the Messerschmitts decided the crazy ship was a bomber and not a fighter. They swarmed upon her, which was exactly what the wild Irishman wanted.

Stan went to work with his guns, but he kept track of the doings of his crazy pilot. O'Malley seemed to have gone stark mad. He plunged up into the path of the oncoming fighters and his banks of Brownings opened up. Lead spattered all over the Hawk and a lot of it came through. But two Messerschmitt One-Tens went down before the flock discovered that this new ship had more wicked fire power than a Spitfire. They zoomed and dived and circled like angry hornets.

"They need a bit of educatin'," O'Malley shouted. "An if they'll be swarmin' around I'll give it to them."

Stan didn't answer because at that moment his hatch cover splintered into a million tiny cracks and a maze of ragged holes, the line of bullets moving across not six inches above his head.

O'Malley decided the only thing was to select a Messerschmitt and run him down. He picked one and roared after it. The ME, confident that he had superior speed, darted away. But he soon discovered this strange ship had plenty more engine than his One-Ten. He banked and shot down. O'Malley dived and was on his tail, slicing away great chunks of the Jerry's ship.

When they came up they were well inside the enemy lines and no Royal Air Force ships were in sight, though the air was full of assorted Jerries.

"Get back on our side of the fence!" Stan shouted.

"Sure, an' it's nicer over here," O'Malley called back.

But a minute later he took Stan's advice. A Messerschmitt came up from below and a Heinkel dived from above with another ME closing in from the rear. The three fighters raked the Hawk as they closed upon her. Her Double-Wasp coughed and sputtered. She kept on running but her zip was gone and oil and air came sucking back inside her. Stan knew it was the sea for him again.

"Mind getting wet?" O'Malley called back cheerfully as he sent the Hawk down and away from the enemy.

"No, you wild man, but I do mind losing this ship," Stan shouted back.

"She isn't lost," O'Malley called back.

They were sliding down and away from the big fight. Even with a crippled motor the Hawk could show her tail to a Messerschmitt. They saw the Spitfires and the Hurricanes now, battling the Jerries up above, keeping them from opening a path for the Stukas. The cruisers and the destroyers were throwing shells into the sky recklessly and at the same time pounding to pieces two floundering Nazi battleships.

"Sure, an' it's a fine show," O'Malley crowed.

He had hardly finished speaking, when the Wasp backfired savagely, shook herself, then died completely.

"Now, you wild Irishman, slide her home if you can," Stan rasped.

"An' what do ye suppose they have carriers for?" O'Malley called back.

"This bus won't set down on a carrier!" Stan snapped.

He looked down and saw the carrier, her deck looking about the size of a banana peeling. Stan figured the chances of landing on the carrier were about one thousand to one, but he realized that would seem like attractive odds to O'Malley.

The Irishman was circling down upon the carrier in a very businesslike manner. So much so that the crew was running about like wild men. The superstructure panel flashed signals neither Stan nor O'Malley could understand. The little men on the deck fired warning rockets and a couple of flares, and then potted at the Hawk with a pompom which splattered the side of the ship.

"A nice welcome to be givin' the King's two best recruits," O'Malley growled.

As Stan looked down, the things that could happen to them ticked through his mind. They could run over the side and be chewed up by the screws, coming up in the wake of the carrier as foam and grease spots. They could top the bow and be smashed under by the monster plowing ahead at thirty knots. They could slap up against the superstructure island and burn there like a huge flare. Stan upped the chances. They were one in a million, not one in a thousand.

He didn't kick or order O'Malley to bail out, which was the sane thing to do. He didn't even think about his own chute.

The sailors were signaling again and there didn't seem to be any welcome letters in the signals. But the deck was clear as O'Malley swung the Hawk into line and set her for the crazy attempt. The panel flipped black and white warnings frantically as they zipped in.

"The wing flaps!" Stan shouted as the idea struck him.

"Sure, an' I'm dumb," O'Malley came back.

He set the flaps and they nosed over dangerously, but they slowed a lot. The carrier was rolling about, trying to take her proper position, which she had deserted when she started fooling with this strange Royal Air Force plane. She was now paying no attention to the Hawk at all.

Shells from the pocket battleship sent up huge columns of water alongside. Stan squinted through a bullet hole in his hatch cover. The forward plane lift was down, leaving a neat but restricted patch of deck.

Four long, pen-shaped bombs whistled down from the sky. The sea swallowed them and a second later belched an eruption of water.

The Hawk was settling fast now and it seemed the carrier would get away from her. O'Malley cut the incidence. The Hawk lifted a bit, lunged forward and slid over the edge. Then it squashed down, hit and plunged. Stan could see the flying bridge and many staring, white faces.

O'Malley was showing a rare amount of knowledge of carrier landings. He stalled the Hawk as the deck opened under her, then clamped her down furiously. There was a thud, dull but solid. The Hawk wrenched around, screamed complainingly, then set herself at landing position.

Stan tossed his arm over his face and set himself for the crash that would tear him apart. The blow did not come. He slid his arm down, and all around the ship a ring of red-faced sailors peered at him, some of them grinning broadly. Then a cheer broke out.

O'Malley was first out of the ship. He plumped down on the deck and faced an of-

ficer who came charging from somewhere.
He saluted solemnly. Standing there, with
his flying suit hanging on his bony frame,
his hawk face peering at the officer, he
looked more like a scarecrow than one of His
Majesty's crack pilots.

"Where did this come from and what is
it?" the officer demanded.

" 'Tis a dive bomber, the very colleen that
smacked that pocket battleship not so far
back. An' 'tis a valuable specimen as must
be delivered to His Majesty's air forces,"
O'Malley said gravely.

"Go up on the bridge and report at once,"
the officer said and his voice was not so
harsh. He had seen the Hawk make a direct
hit on the deck of the Nazi battleship.

They clumped up to the bridge, Stan edg-
ing in ahead of O'Malley. There ought to
be a bit of diplomacy used and he was afraid
O'Malley might not use the proper approach
to the skipper. The flag officer, who had
piloted them to the bridge, saluted smartly
and retired. Stan faced a grizzled man of
about sixty. Steel-blue eyes regarded him
frostily. Then the commander smiled.

"My compliments, gentlemen," he said.

"A mighty fine effort though a bit risky."

"Thank you, sir," Stan answered. "This plane is a test job and we felt she was so valuable she ought to be salvaged."

"I see, so you set that superdemon down on my deck." He gave Stan a searching look. "Your navy training is good. How does it come that you are not with the sea forces?"

"My friend, Lieutenant O'Malley, made the landing, sir," Stan said.

O'Malley grinned broadly at the commander. "Sure, an' it was pure luck, the luck o' the Irish," he said.

"You will be cared for and your specimen plane will be landed," the commander promised. "In fact, I watched you dive bomb that battleship and I believe the navy could use some of this type of ship. I will make a memorandum to that effect."

As they walked down from the bridge, Stan looked at O'Malley. "I never asked you where you learned to fly," he said. "Could it have been the Royal Navy?"

"It could have been," O'Malley answered and closed his big mouth tight.

Stan didn't ask any more questions. They

went below and had a good meal.   Later they received word from the commander that the carrier was headed across to the Norwegian coast, but they would be sent home by motor launch.   The Hendee Hawk would have to wait until the naval patrol swung around their course and slipped into Portsmouth, or some other port.

"How long will the swing take?"   Stan asked.

The young officer who had delivered the message shook his head.   "One never knows."

They had to be satisfied with that.   No one could tell what the squadron would run into, or when their course would be changed. Nor, of course, whether the carrier would ever see port again.   In the meantime all they could do was trust to luck that the Hawk would be delivered ashore somehow.   They were fortunate that they were being sent back by a motor launch and wouldn't have to accompany the squadron across to the Norwegian coast.

CHAPTER VIII

O'MALLEY and Stan climbed out of a
Bentley roadster and hurried across the
street to the squadron gateway. The sentry
let them pass after one look at their soiled
uniforms and a brief word.

"We'll be collectin' a bushel of medals in
about a minute," O'Malley said.

"We'll probably lose a strip of hide for
not bringing the Hawk home," Stan replied
grimly.

They entered the mess and found a large
number of men about. The rousing welcome
O'Malley had forecast was lacking. A number of the boys looked at them, then turned
away. There was something in the air, a
definite tightness caused by their entering
that Stan didn't like at all. The Irishman
barged cheerfully across the room and ordered a pie.

Stan sank into a chair. Without appearing to be interested, except in the paper he had picked up, he watched the men in the room. They were looking at him and there was hostility in the glances they shot his way.

Tossing aside the paper, he got to his feet. There was one quick way to find out. He'd collar one of the boys and put it up to him, demanding a straight answer. He was moving across the room, when an orderly spoke to him. Stan swung around. The orderly was nervous and kept his eyes roving everywhere but upon the Flight Lieutenant.

"Wing Commander Farrell wishes to speak to you, sir," he reported.

"Thanks, I'll be right over," Stan answered.

Stan guessed what had happened. Garret had tracked him down. Possibly had seen him. Stan stepped over to O'Malley. The Irishman, his mouth full of pie, turned around. He glanced at Stan, then shoved aside the remainder of his pie.

"Sure, an' you been seein' a ghost." Then his big mouth clamped shut tight. After a moment's thought, he added, "If they try givin' you a ride for the job I did, I'm in on it."

"No, O'Malley." Stan shoved out his hand. "But if I don't see you again, here's luck."

O'Malley looked at the hand, shook his red thatch and glared at Stan. "By the bomb rack of a Stuka," he snarled, "I'm standing by. Let's go get the spalpeen that's makin' the stink!"

Stan grinned in spite of himself. At that moment O'Malley would have laid a bony fist on the jaw of an Air Marshal. He had never seen the Irishman so wrought-up; he was twice as mad as he ever got when he went into action.

"This is something only Stan Wilson can handle." Then he added more softly, "It hasn't anything to do with the little show we put on. And you can't help me. Thanks, just the same."

O'Malley stood glaring after him as he went out, then he faced the man in the mess and his eyes were snapping dangerously.

Stan went straight to headquarters and an orderly let him into the Wing Commander's office without delay. The instant he stepped into the room Stan knew his whole world had blown up under him. Beside the

O.C.'s desk sat Charles L. Milton and across from him was Garret, smiling triumphantly and smugly. He leaned forward as Stan hesitated at the door.

"Come in, Wilson," Farrell said curtly.

"How are you, Stan?" Milton said. He was clearly upset over what he had been listening to before Stan arrived.

"I am fine, thanks."

Garret said nothing. He just leaned back with a sneer on his lips.

"You wished to speak to me, sir?"

"Sit down, Wilson." Farrell straightened some papers on his desk, cleared his throat, then looked at the young flier. "Lieutenant Garret has laid your former record before me and Mr. Milton has confirmed it." The Wing Commander paused and his eyes followed the lines of the report. He looked up and his eyes bored into Stan. "You were charged with selling plans of the Hendee Hawk to Nazi agents." Stan knew he was supposed to answer.

"I was tried and acquitted."

"That is true, but no American firm would hire you and the Army refused to allow you to enlist. Is that correct?"

"Yes, sir."

The Wing Commander cleared his throat. "Have you anything to say for yourself that would clear up this angle?"

"I was the victim of Nazi agents who stole the plans. That was proved at the trial. Later, they cleverly planted rumors and suspicions about me so that no one wanted to have anything to do with me. In plain American, I was framed." Stan spoke slowly, putting all the conviction he could into his words. He didn't expect the O.C. to believe him any more than the American firms or the army officers to whom he had applied for entry into the service.

"You have done a splendid job here, for which the British people and His Majesty's Government thank you; but, in these times of great danger, we cannot take chances with anyone whose past record is in doubt. I am sorry, Wilson, but I have orders to release you and send you back to the United States."

Stan sat looking at the Wing Commander. Suddenly anger boiled up inside him, a savage, cold anger.

"If you can show no more appreciation

than this, I do not care to stay. My record with the Royal Air Force should be proof that the charges against me were phony."

The O.C. reddened. He looked at Garret. Scowling blackly, he said, "I took that attitude, personally, but my superior officers have ordered your release."

"Before you release him I suggest that you consider another angle," Garret said. "I have just learned that, though he and an Irish recruit returned safely, the new plane did not return. The fighters of all groups have been questioned and they did not see the Hawk in action against the enemy at all. I think the plane was delivered to Nazi agents on the coast." Garret's voice was little better than a snarl when he finished.

Stan's gaze locked with that of the lieutenant. "The Hendee Hawk will be delivered here at the field in a few days. Lieutenant O'Malley set her down on a carrier in the channel after she was put out of action."

Garret laughed harshly. "That is a fine story, Wilson, but one that only a fool would believe."

"It is an impossible story," the O.C. agreed.

"He should be locked up," Garret insisted.

"I hardly think that will be necessary," a voice from the doorway said. The men turned and saw Allison standing just inside the room, supported by the strong arm of O'Malley.

"Sure, an' did I hear someone say I didn't set that Hawk down on a carrier?" O'Malley growled. His glare traveled from Farrell to Garrett and fastened there. Garret shrank back in his chair.

The pair moved into the room. Allison's face was white and thin but his eyes were snapping. The Wing Commander frowned.

"This is an intrusion. Remember, gentlemen, you are junior officers." Farrell fixed O'Malley with a cold glare as the Irishman pulled forward a chair for Allison.

"We felt it of great importance, sir," Allison said as he sank into the chair. "I am sure you will agree when I explain." He took a thick envelope from his pocket and laid it on the desk before the O.C. "These papers will be of interest to you, sir, I am sure."

The Wing Commander opened the envelope and spread a sheaf of papers on his desk. He bent over them, reading deliberately.

After laying aside the last report he looked up. His eyes were on Garret.

"It seems, Lieutenant, that you have made a jackass out of yourself and out of me. These reports are from the American Federal Bureau of Investigation, and from the British Intelligence. Both departments give Lieutenant Wilson a clean slate. Both report he was, as he says, 'framed.'" He turned to Stan.

"With these reports you could join the United States Army Air Corps any time you wished. After the treatment you have received here I feel it my duty to offer you a release so that you may do so."

The sudden turn of affairs had Stan groggy; however, the realization that he was at last freed of the smear that had blackened his name started a surge of warmth and elation through him. He turned to Allison.

"You knew it all the time," he accused.

Allison grinned. "Yes, that report came in with your credentials. I took it out of the file to have a bit of sport with you. It was dumb of me to forget to replace it. But you were so stubborn over the whole matter I didn't feel you needed to know."

Garret got to his feet. His face was white and his voice was not very steady. "I merely did my duty as I saw it, sir. I had no way of knowing what was in the report Allison has laid before you. I ask leave to retire."

"Stay where you are. I want to talk to you," the O.C. snapped.

Stan got to his feet. Milton was thumping him on the back and O'Malley was grinning like a wolf. Milton rumbled in his deep voice:

"I said it all smelled fishy to me." He turned to the O.C. "Wilson is the best test pilot that ever stepped into a plane."

"Allison's comin' back in a couple days an' Red Flight goes out in Spitfires," O'Malley broke in eagerly. "Sure, an' there's no war on over in America. 'Tis right here you'll be staying or I'll give you a fine dusting when we get outside."

"I'm staying until the war is over. In a way I figure it's our fight, too, sir. If you don't mind, I'll stay in Red Flight."

"Mind! I'll recommend you for top honors." The O.C. was beaming.

An orderly stepped into the room and laid a report on Farrell's desk. He glanced at it, then picked it up. A minute later he pounded the desk with his fist and began to laugh.

"This report says His Majesty's carrier, *Staunch,* has on board a new type of dive bomber which put a pocket battleship out of action and later landed upon the deck of the carrier. The commander considers the plane so valuable he is putting in to deliver it."

"Until we can get three of those Hawks for you boys, you will fly Spitfires as Red Flight," the O.C. said. "After that you will likely win the war without any help."

"Sure, an' we'll do just that, sor, as a special favor to you," O'Malley answered.

The O.C. looked at him and frowned. He wasn't sure whether O'Malley was spoofing or meant it. Allison and Stan were sure O'Malley was in dead earnest.

"Thank you, sir," Stan said. "We'll run along now."

When they were outside the office, Allison said in his slow drawl:

"That ought to be the last of Garret."

"Sure, an' he'll be brewin' trouble if he stays around, you can bank on that," O'Malley said.

Stan had the same feeling. There was something about Garret he could not understand. He had a feeling there was more than just a grudge against him in Garret's acts. The lieutenant had certain connections that seemed to reach very high up into official circles. Stan planned to do some quiet checking, now that he didn't have to be so careful.

During the next three days Stan poked about asking a lot of questions. He was very careful not to arouse suspicion. He learned very little. Garret came in as a ferry pilot and later was given a chance in the air. He was a Canadian who had lived most of his life in the United States. Why he was not released from the Air Arm after Allison reported his action in deserting Red Flight was not clear. And no one seemed to know how he had managed to get himself placed in a responsible position close to the O.C.

One thing looked good to Stan. Garret had left the squadron and no one knew where he had been sent. He was out of the way, yet

Stan had a feeling he had not seen the last of him.

The day Allison returned to duty an order was posted creating a night defense group of fighters. It consisted of twelve Spitfires and Red Flight was included. O'Malley was so excited over the order that he walked away from a half pie, forgetting it entirely.

"Sure, an' this is me dish," he crowed.

"Swatting Stukas in the dark?" Allison asked grimly. "Dodging balloon cables and ducking through Ack-Ack muck?"

"This Moon Flight is the toughest job in the service," Stan admitted. "But we should be swelled up. Look at the list of boys posted."

"Oh, yes," Allison admitted. "All aces." He laughed shortly.

"You've recovered all right," Stan said with a grin.

There was reason enough for setting aside twelve of the toughest, most reckless, Spitfire pilots for night service. London had been smashed and battered and set on fire night after night. The ground guns and the balloons got a few of the bandits, but too many slipped through and sent their cargoes

of death down upon the city. It was up to
the boys with the eight-gun death in their
wind edges to stop the invaders.

The first action came at eleven o'clock that
evening. The call for the new formation
blasted into the mess while the men were
gathered around speculating on who would
draw the job of being Squadron Leader.
They rushed out into the night after hurrying into their togs. On the cab rank an even
dozen Spitfires breathed flame from idling
motors, trembling like things alive, straining
to be up and into the blackness after the
skulking killers.

Allison stumbled out after O'Malley, and
Stan came behind the Britisher. They got
their flight orders, tested their throttles, then
pinched wheel brakes and slipped around
and down upon the line. They would go up
in threes. Red Flight was third out and
O'Malley fumed into his flap mike over the
delay.

The Recording Officer, looking massive in
his greatcoat, backed away. A mobile floodlight slid over the field and took position, its
long, wide beam slapping down the runway.

"Steady, Moon Flight, check your temperatures," ordered the Squadron Leader.

Stan stiffened as the voice came in over his headset. He knew that voice. It was the voice of Arch Garret!

Affirmative replies clicked in. Stan managed to answer, but his mind was in a hard knot. This was all cockeyed. Garret leading a flight that called for the toughest of flying. Stan groaned. This would be a lucky night for the Jerries, and a tough break for the folks crouching in the darkened streets. He heard the banshee wail of the alarm sirens as he slid his hatch cover into place.

"East. Contact bandits at 8,000 feet. Moon Flight east," Garret's voice gritted into Stan's ears.

The Spitfires roared up and away to the east. Every pilot was straining to catch a glimpse of the incoming raiders. They spread out and bored into the darkness, swooping and diving, but they made no contacts. Behind them the searchlights stabbed and crisscrossed and wavered. Then the ground guns began to blast, and tracer bullets arched upward like rockets in a celebration. The muck over lower London was thick and the searchlights began to pick out black shapes. Then came the bombs. They smashed into roofs and went splintering on to blow houses to bits. They rent and ripped mortar and stone and brick. People were buried under the debris.

Stan banked steeply and shouted into his flap mike. "They've slipped in behind us. Come on, Red Flight!"

"Sure, an' I'm way ahead of ye," came the voice of O'Malley.

Moon Flight wheeled and went thundering back. They could not stop the raging fires below or do anything about the shattered buildings, but they could make sure that few of the raiders ever made a return trip.

In the dull glow from the fires below Stan saw O'Malley's ship dive down, like a streak of dark shadow, straight upon a Junkers that was flying along in a manner that suggested it thought it was over unprotected territory. O'Malley's guns drilled fire and the Junkers' right wing flipped upward and faded into the night. Then the killer nosed over and went down like a flaming torch.

Stan was into the battle before the wrecked Junkers had dropped 500 feet. He laid over and raked a big death ship with his

Brownings. It folded and slid off, spewing its crew into the night.

Having made contact Moon Flight really went to work. Their first savage attack had broken up the spear-shaped Stuka formation. Now they gave their attention to individual combat. There was no need for commands from anyone. They swung about on invisible hairpins and screamed after the big fellows.

It didn't take so very long. Stuka after Stuka went down. From the black pit above the Jerry fighters were diving down to see what had happened to their charges. The Messerschmitts twisted and ducked and dived, clearing their guns for action.

Down at the 4,000-foot level the Spitfires were knocking down the last of the raiders. This done, they nosed upward to meet the Messerschmitts as eagerly as they had attacked the killers. They were overeager to contact the fighters and one of them caught a crossfire as he roared in. His ship went slithering off to the west, spinning madly. The Spits darted through the flame filled sky. They flipped over and spun and dived, always seeking targets to make their guns flame.

Stan sent his Spitfire into a screaming reversement, tipped out of it with his guns hammering as he laid his sights on a leering swastika. It was over quickly. The Messerschmitts had no stomach for such a deadly game. After a gesture at rescuing their bombers, they fled into the night.

"Moon Flight, come in. Moon Flight, come in."

Then O'Malley's brogue burred. "Begorra, 'tis a very fine avening."

Stan grinned. He was glad to hear the voice of the wild Irishman. After a battle in the sky the voice of a pal always sounds good. He bent forward.

"The same to you, Irisher."

"And to you, Yank," came Allison's voice.

They slid in like mottled ghosts and Stan counted them. Nine Spitfires. There would be three new faces in Moon Flight tomorrow. Three new men for the raider shift. He toyed with the idea of slipping by and checking Garret's guns, but gave it up. Garret would be wise enough to fire a burst or two.

And, of course, he might have misjudged the lieutenant.

In the briefing room there was little talk. The boys were grim and sour. London had been bombed. They got little comfort out of the impressive score they had chalked up— ten Stukas and six Messerschmitts. They knew that if they had headed west they would have stopped the raid.

No one challenged Garret when he claimed one Stuka and a Messerschmitt. Nobody spoke to him. They went on into the mess and flopped down to wait for the metallic voice of the intersquadron speaker.

O'Malley lay on a bench with his feet up against the wall. Allison lay back, his eyes closed, his thin face colorless. Stan sat staring at the floor. He was trying to get a lot of things straight in his mind. He couldn't honestly say Garret had led them east purposely. The main control room must have sent them in the wrong direction, but it all bothered him, anyway. And he knew the other boys had the same feeling.

CHAPTER IX

SPECIAL MISSION

STAN was further mystified the next day when Garret came to him in the mess. He was smiling and very friendly.

"I have been a rotter, Wilson," he said and held out his hand. "After all, this is pretty serious business and there isn't much place for personal grudges and gripes."

Stan hid his surprise. He could find no words to answer Garret. He shook hands with the Squadron Leader. Garret slapped him on the back.

"I have the toughest gang of sky-busters in the whole Royal Air Force," Garret said. "We'll see that no more bombs land on London."

As he walked away Stan looked after him. Now that Garret had left him he could think of several things he might have said. Allison came up and there was a mocking leer on his face.

"So you are teacher's pet from now on?"

"Search me, but I still don't think he likes me," Stan said.

"He's about to collar O'Malley." Allison chuckled. "I'd give a new shilling to hear what that Irishman tells him."

It happened they were near enough, because O'Malley bawled out what he had to say so loudly it could have been heard out on the field. Garret had halted and was smilingly giving O'Malley the glad hand. He stepped back a pace and his face flushed as the Irisher cut loose.

"Sure, an' ye can save yer blarney!" O'Malley roared. "I'd as soon hang one on that hooked beak of yours as to be after lookin' at ye!"

Garret backed up a step and lifted one hand. Stan and Allison could not hear what he said, but the officers near the pair were openly grinning. O'Malley loosed one more blast and his words brought chill, brittle silence to the room.

"I'm a thinkin' you'd best head the Moon

Flight in the right direction when the spalpeens come over again.''

The clicking of Garret's heels was the only
sound in the room. He marched out without
a word. Everyone looked about uneasily.
Such talk to a Squadron Leader was un-
heard of. Any other commander would have
had O'Malley's hide off in a minute and
draped all over the place. The very fact that
the Irishman had gotten away with it had a
depressing effect upon the fliers. Allison
broke the spell. He barged over to O'Malley
and shoved out his hand.

''Shake, Irisher,'' he said.

Judd, McCumber, and Kelley, all men who
had belonged to the first spread Stan had
been with, strolled over and a little group
formed around O'Malley. Judd squinted up
at the lank Irishman. He was a short,
chubby-faced youngster of nineteen. His
face was beaming happily.

''I'd never had the courage to talk like
that to a Squadron Leader. I just went into
a funk when he soaped me.''

O'Malley squinted down at Judd. '' 'Tis
with me own eyes I saw you cut the fire of

three Messers, me bye. Don't you be blatherin' me about courage.''

Judd flushed. He was all right when he was up there by himself, but he was bashful in a crowd. McCumber looked across at Allison.

"Red Flight should get a break after this,'' he said meaningly.

Allison grinned wolfishly. "Really, now, Mac, Garret knows every boy in Moon Flight loves him.''

Kelley had not spoken nor had he laughed with the others. "He'd better stay out of my circle. I have folks living out beyond Kensington Gardens.''

No one said anything more about the raids. They all knew Kelley's home had been smashed that night and that his father had been injured. Allison changed the subject.

"We certainly should get rid of Garret for the good of the service. He's no fit leader and the squadron will go into a funk under him.''

"How will we do it?'' Mac asked.

"I don't know, but it has to be done. A decent leader would have wiped the floor with

O'Malley and then grounded him for the rest of the war. A yellow streak has no place in this outfit."

The men nodded their heads. What they could not understand was how Garret had gotten the job. They felt helpless because they had always depended upon the men at headquarters. Finally the group broke up without anyone offering a workable plan.

Just after noon the next day the O.C. sent for Stan. He was alone in his office and in very good spirits. Stan sat down beside his desk and waited.

"We have a few Hendee Hawks coming in," Farrell beamed happily. "You are the man to handle them and to show the boys their fine points. In fact, you're the only man we have who can do it quickly. We need those superfighters badly. Headquarters would like to do a little daylight bombing. Do you think a flight of Hawks could take a squadron of Liberators through?"

"They could," Stan assured him. "Give me nine Hawks and my pick of pilots and we'll ride right in over Berlin."

"You won't get nine for a while, but we

have three coming in." The Wing Commander seemed interested in what Stan thought of that.

"Three will take a small flight through," Stan said.

"I have to depend on you, Wilson. Without you, it will take several weeks to get them lined out and set for action."

"We need train only one man. Allison can learn quickly." Stan smiled broadly. "O'Malley learned in a couple of flights."

The O.C. smiled, too. "Yes, your pie-eating friend will handle one, if we can drill some sense into his head."

"O'Malley's crazy but it's the sort of lunacy we need," Stan answered dryly.

Farrell nodded. He was already thinking about other things. "The Royal Air Force considered this shipment so important they routed the freighter north to avoid submarines and Stukas. It seems Nazi agents found out when she left. She had quite a trip and was chased far north, damaged by a sub and finally landed at our naval base in the Shetlands."

"We pick them up up there?"

"I'm sending you up there to service them and get them ready. When you have them set up and ready to fly, I'll send Allison and O'Malley up there to help you bring them back."

Stan waited but the O.C. had nothing more to say, so he got to his feet.

"When do I leave?"

"As soon as you can get away."

"Do I fly a Spitfire?"

The O.C. considered this for a long minute. At last he nodded. "You're too valuable a man to be shot down by stray raiders."

"I'll be on my way in an hour," Stan said as he snapped a salute.

As Stan swung out of the office he almost collided with Garret.

"Whoa there, you're in a big rush, aren't you?" Garret asked with a grin.

"Sorry," Stan grunted and was off.

As he strode across the field he got to wondering if Garret had been listening at the door. It didn't seem possible. Eavesdropping in an officer of Garret's standing would have laughed him out of the service if he had been caught. He dismissed it from his mind.

He told Allison and O'Malley about his plans and warned them not to mention his trip to anyone. Allison grinned lazily. O'Malley was excited.

"Sure, an' the war's about over," he boasted. "With me coaxing one of them sweet colleens through the skies there won't be a Jerry left in a week."

"You lugs come a-rattling when I send in the call," Stan said as he strode toward his quarters.

A half-hour later he was kicking his Spitfire into line. He was into the air swiftly and laid his course across the serene green countryside to pick up the shore of the North Sea at the nearest point.

At that height it was difficult to realize he was in the sky above a war-torn nation. There were no evidences of destruction below, and the blue sky was clear of enemy planes. The steady throbbing roar of the Spitfire's motor was a pleasantly lulling sound, and he settled back comfortably with his mind at ease, checking over the structural details of the Hendee Hawks in his mind for use in putting the dismantled ships together as fast as possible when he landed at the naval base where they awaited him.

It was pleasant to be out of danger for this brief period. It gave him a chance to examine his thoughts, do a little readjusting of his personal concepts to the grim realities of war. He found he had been under such terrific tension every instant since reporting to the Red Flight that this was the first chance he had found to look back over what had happened and realize how supremely lucky he had been thus far to escape death.

Flying at 4,000 feet, he appeared to be merely creeping across the green blanket of England beneath him. Ahead, he could faintly see a silver line of mist marking the shore of the sea. Though the Spitfire was tunneling through the blue at 350 miles an hour, he suddenly found he was impatient for even more speed. Behind him men were even now fighting and dying. He wanted to get back into it, start doing his part again.

An alien sound obtruded suddenly into the throbbing of his Spitfire. He heard it almost without consciousness of what it portended, then was abruptly aware that a stream of bullets was ripping through his fuselage.

A Heinkel had slid up behind him from no-where and its smoking guns were streaming hot, leaden death at him. For a moment he was too amazed to properly meet this unexpected danger. He had a curious feeling that it was after *him*. That it wasn't merely a stray enemy plane making chance contact. It was an absurd thought, but it gripped him strongly and he couldn't shake it off.

Another burst of lead hosed from the Heinkel. Stan rolled the Spitfire to the left, then pulled it up tight and hard. The Heinkel shot under him, went into a loop, then faked a turnover. Stan smiled grimly.

"That won't fool me, son," he muttered. He leveled off fast and eased over into a three hundred yard safety zone. Setting the Spit on her ear, he faced the Heinkel, testing his Brownings as he slid into place.

The Jerry was a crack flier. The Heinkel came in with a roaring thrust, her Madsen slugs drilling away at the Spitfire. Stan heard the stingers zipping through his fuselage. A blue flame began playing up and down over a hole in his fuel tank.

"Well," Stan muttered sourly. "I'll have to put a stop to this, or else——"

He sent the Spitfire off to the right like a streak. The Heinkel zoomed past, building altitude for a death thrust. Stan cracked the throttle wide open and kicked in the emergency booster. The Merlin answered splendidly.

Glancing into his mirror he took in the setup, then faked a steep climb. Up he went, 500 feet, then sent the Spitfire into a screaming back-over roll, holding his ship upside down until he was behind the Heinkel and above it. Then he dropped the Spitfire as though she were crippled. This placed him under the Heinkel and he went up. The Jerry was now trying to make a run for it. Stan saw a spread of fuselage and a wing through his windscreen and he pressed the gun button. The Brownings spat fire and lead. The Jerry was trapped and knew it. He swayed and rocked and twisted in an attempt to get away. The bullets drilled out again, a four-second burst.

Fire and smoke rolled out of the port motor. The flames licked in around the stricken ship. A rancid whiff came to Stan and reminded him that his own fuel tank was on fire. It would be only a matter of seconds until he would be in a flaming coffin himself.

The Merlin was still hitting beautifully. Stan squirmed about and jerked loose a fire extinguisher. He turned the handle and pumped frantically. The liquid spray feathered out and blanketed the fire. Stan sucked in a deep breath and looked down at the plummeting Heinkel. The Jerry was trying to bail out, but he wasn't making much headway. Stan nosed down and watched the struggle.

He was sorry for the pilot but it was not pity that made him circle lower and check the field toward which the Heinkel was spinning. Stan wanted to ask that Jerry a few questions, and the Jerry had to be rescued from his firetrap or he couldn't do it.

The Heinkel turned over, flattened and eased up, then plunged into a tangle of bushes beside a road. Stan gauged the rolling field which spread beside the road. He could have set a Hurricane down on that field easily, but a Spitfire was different. Her landing gear was high and narrow. He side-slipped and leveled off, then skimmed over the grass and bumped down, jerking and swaying. The Spitfire rolled up to within a safe distance from the burning plane and Stan leaped out.

The Jerry had almost made it out of the plane. He was draped over the side with his parachute harness caught in the smashed hatch cover. Risking an explosion which would have finished them both, Stan jerked the pilot loose and dragged him a safe distance from his ship. They were less than fifty feet from the Heinkel, when her tank cut loose and billows of smoke and flame rolled up, licking at the grass and brush.

The Heinkel's pilot sat on the grass. He watched his ship vanish and his face worked. If it had not been for the Royal Air Force pilot bending over him, he would at that moment be frying to a crisp. He shuddered and licked his lips.

Stan gave his attention to the fellow's wounds. He was badly hit in the shoulder and bleeding freely. His face was white.

"Who tipped you off that I'd be flying solo along this route?" Stan demanded.

The Nazi lifted blue eyes to Stan and shook his head grimly.

"Better talk, son, you are bleeding plenty."

"That would be revealing a military secret," the Nazi said in clipped English.

"I suppose you think I followed regulations and war rules in ducking down into this pile of rocks to drag you out of your crate?" Stan's eyes were cold and hard.

The Jerry coughed and smiled weakly. "I am indebted to you," he said slowly.

"If I don't get you to a doctor, you'll be as bad off as if you were still in that bonfire," Stan snapped. "Talk and I'll see what I can do. And hand me that Luger." He reached down and jerked the officer's gun from him. The Nazi had been too weak to make fast use of it.

"I suppose you are right." The officer coughed again and his hand slipped to his breast where his tunic was fast becoming soaked with blood.

"I might as well talk." Fear was showing in his eyes.

"Good. Who tipped you off?"

"A man who has quite an inside position

with you. His name is—" The Jerry
paused and coughed.

"Yes?" Stan bent and steadied him. He
was afraid the Nazi would pass out before he
spoke again.

"Arch Garret," the Nazi said, then went
limp in Stan's arms.

Stan stared down in the gray face for a
moment. His lips were drawn into a tight
line and his eyes were blazing. Then he remembered his promise to the unconscious
Nazi. Picking the man up he carried him to
the stone fence which separated the field
from the road.

An old car had halted and a man and a
woman sat staring at the smoking Nazi plane
and the trim Spitfire. When Stan appeared
they started to get the old car into action.

"Wait!" Stan shouted.

The man recognized Stan's uniform and a
broad smile came to his lips. He halted the
car and waited while Stan carried the
wounded man to the roadside.

"Can you get him to a doctor at once?" he
asked.

"Verra easy," the man said.

"Take him to a doctor, then notify your

authorities that you have a Nazi prisoner. You should get a handsome reward for such a prize. He is a pilot and pilots are valuable."

The man and the woman began to talk at the same time. Stan loaded the wounded officer into the back seat and waved to the pair. Turning, he headed for his Spitfire.

Stan plugged the hole in his gas tank and warmed the Spitfire a bit, then rolled her to the far end of the field. There was some question as to whether he could make off the rough field, but he was in a terrible hurry and did not care to wait for help.

With a last careful survey of the grass runway he was off. The Spitfire rocked and dipped her wings and swayed drunkenly, but she lifted and cleared the stone fence. Now that he was in the air Stan had to decide what he should do about Arch Garret. As he circled for altitude, he tried to figure it out.

He had a hunch Garret was just a cog in a bad machine. He was the logical man to shove into the middle of things and the British were eagerly picking up overseas pilots. The Royal Air Force was well filled with

Australians, New Zealanders, Canadians, and others from the empire at large. Garret was a Canadian citizen, even though he had spent his last few years in the United States. Now it was very clear why Moon Flight had missed the bombers until they had done their work of destruction.

The question was whether he should fly back and report—or whether he should call Wing Commander Farrell and have secret agents put on Garret's trail. Garret would undoubtedly have an airtight alibi. And he certainly had backing that went high up. Stan might just make a fool out of himself. After all, the whole thing sounded like a tall story.

He finally decided to go on to the navy base and then send for Allison and O'Malley at once. They would believe him and help him. He would have a good crew of mechanics at the field to slap the Hawks together quickly and might be able to get them off in one day. Then there was one other thing that tipped the balance in favor of going on. This was pretty much a personal matter between himself and Arch Garret. This was the second time Garret had tried to wipe him out.

Heading north he drove along and did not see any more Heinkels. He was hailed by a scouting squadron from the fleet arm.

"Where to, Spitfire?" called a very English voice over the radio.

"Navy base. Shetlands," Stan called back.

"Good luck and cheerio, Yank," came back the English voice.

Stan grinned broadly. His western accent sure marked him well. He bored ahead, his eyes seeing far into the distance, his mind working upon the crooked plotting of Arch Garret.

He spotted the naval base and circled around to give the boys at the batteries a chance to see who he was, then set down and turned the Spitfire over to a ground crew. Taking his file of papers he headed for the commander's quarters.

The commander was an affable man, ruddy-faced and square-jawed. He had heard about Stan and O'Malley's attack upon the pocket battleship.

"I was so inquisitive about those ships I had them unloaded and uncovered. They

are beauties, sir.   But I can't see what you'll
want with so much motor.''

"I'll show you," Stan promised. "Now I
want to make a call back to London and then
I want a squad of your best mechanics.   I
have to get these Hawks into action at once.''

"You will get all the help you can use,"
the commander promised.

Stan got Wing Commander Farrell on the
wire and talked to him.   He did not report
the brush with the Heinkel, though he would
have to mention it in his written report.
And he did not mention Arch Garret.   When
he asked that Allison and O'Malley be sent
up at once, the O.C. hesitated.

"We have been having poor luck keeping
the bombers out," he said. "I'll have to replace you three and add six more Spitfires,
if I can get them.''

"I need them at once.   The sooner you get
them up here, the sooner we'll be back to
help you.''

"I have an old Defiant they can both pile
into," the O.C. finally said. "I'll get them
off tomorrow before daylight.''

Stan waited a few minutes, then put in a

call for Allison. Presently the Britisher's drawl came in over the wire clearly:

"What's the matter, Yank, grounded in some cow pasture?"

"I landed in one but didn't like it," Stan said with a laugh. "I'm calling from the navy base."

"What's up?"

"Just this. I'm sending for you fellows and you will get orders to leave just before daylight. Look out for clouds. Fly that old Defiant low and watch for Heinkels. And tonight, if there's a raid, just you duck in the opposite direction from the way the Squadron Leader orders. I'll spin you a yarn when you get up here. Keep mum but pass the word to the boys to follow you if there's a raid."

"Well, really, old man, you know O'Malley and I can keep still and we can get orders mixed up badly."

"See you tomorrow." Stan hung up.

That night Stan slept soundly. He was still snoring away when the bugler outside his window blew first call. The moment his eyes opened he tossed aside the blankets and

jumped out of bed. He wolfed his breakfast
and was out on the field and headed for the
hangar where the three Hawks were taking
flying shape.

Allison and O'Malley came in before nine
o'clock. Allison was flying the ship. He
smiled thinly at Stan as he climbed out.

"I brought her up here. When you men-
tioned Heinkels, O'Malley was for hunting
in the clouds a bit."

"I hated to waste a good trip," O'Malley
complained.

"The boys at the factory sent the Hawks
out almost ready to fly. We'll be in London
tonight," Stan said.

O'Malley's eyes were on the three Hawks
which had been rolled out into the sunshine
in front of the hangar.

" 'Twill be swell flyin' a ship that hasn't
been all daubed up and smeared with messy
paint," he said.

"We'll fly them in without camouflage,"
Stan agreed.

Five minutes later O'Malley and Allison
were helping with the Hawks. O'Malley was
burning up to be off, but the fighters had to

be carefully checked. As they worked Allison told Stan how they had been chased by three Messerschmitts.

"If you hadn't warned us, and if we hadn't decided to change our time of departure, we might have had plenty of trouble," Allison said.

Stan came around from behind one of the Hawks. "I might as well tell you the whole yarn while the boys are tuning up the motors," he said.

They sat on a bench in the sun while Stan told what had happened to him on his trip over. When he came to the part about making the Jerry talk, and name Garret, O'Malley leaped to his feet.

"Splinter me rudder!" he shouted. "I'm fer kitin' back this minnit. Wait till I get me hands on that spalpeen!"

"No use to go off half-cocked," Stan warned. "We need to catch Garret redhanded. I figure we'll get a few real spies along with him. But we won't be on schedule. Garret has a way of finding out what's going on in the O.C.'s office. He will tip off the Nazis and they'll be waiting to gang up on us."

"Sure, an' that's just what we want," O'Malley broke in. "They gang up an' we spatter the smithereens out of them."

Stan shook his head, but he had to laugh, O'Malley looked so wild. "We'll be doing much better service trapping Garret and his rats."

"Stan is right, old fellow," Allison said grimly.

"I want to know what you fellows think of our handling this just among ourselves? We can keep Garret from sidetracking Moon Flight when a raid comes over. And we can round up the snakes he's working with at the same time."

"How about tonight? Suppose the Jerries hit tonight?" Allison asked.

"We'll get off early and be there for any raid. I'll ask the naval commander not to report us out until midnight. That will throw Garret off," Stan said.

"How soon can we hit the trail?" O'Malley asked.

"Two or three hours will have them in shape. You come with me and I'll show you all you need to know about a Hawk to make her do things," he said to Allison.

Stan and Allison headed toward the nearest ship. O'Malley stretched himself out in the sun and closed his eyes. He figured he already knew more about a Hawk than the Hendee aeronautical officials.

CHAPTER X

GROUND SLEUTHING

THREE Hendee Hawks nosed out across the navy field and roared south. Stan's ship formed the spearhead of a sharp V. O'Malley refused to keep still. He sang and talked about everything he could think of, which was a wide range of subjects. Allison held the right hand slot and said nothing. Stan held the big motor up ahead of him at a pace that would have ripped the pistons out of any other ship. He felt at home with the engine up in front of him instead of at his back.

The take-off had been later than he had planned, but with the terrific cruising speed the Hawks could maintain, they would reach London early. Dusk filled the earth below and the stars came out. Stan couldn't shake off the feeling that there was need for speed. He could not drive that uneasiness out of his mind or bury it under other thoughts. He was sure Allison was as worried as he. O'Malley didn't appear to have a worry at all.

Hours later they sighted London. They sighted it because of the thick muck of flaming shells and the searchlights knifing back and forth through the mass of bursting steel. The Jerries were at it again and seemed to have slipped inside the balloons and the ring of Ack-Ack guns.

"Looks like more of Garret's dirty work," Allison snarled.

"That sneakin' spalpeen! Just let me cross his trail this night. He'll find out what sixteen Brownings can do," O'Malley rumbled.

"Don't shoot him down," Stan ordered grimly. "And keep your mouth shut about him."

The three Hendee Hawks came roaring down upon the nice party the Jerries had planned. The Spitfires were up, but they were off their contact. Though they were now roaring back to give battle, they were too late to save the city from a terrible beating, unless the Hawks succeeded in breaking up the formation. Stan imagined he could hear the Stuka leader's voice crackling in over the radio.

"Left wheel, dive bombers 6, 8, 10 attack positions 27, 39, 49."

He knew such a command had been given because a mass of Stukas, marked clearly by the searchlights and the fires below, were swooping down. They were very low over the city, far below the Hawks.

"Peel off and go into action. Break the spearhead," Stan snapped into his flap mike.

The Hawks peeled off and went down, O'Malley first, then Stan, and then Allison. The drone of their motors was terrific and their pilots were slapped back against their shock pads and held there. Down Stan went, straight for the leading Stuka. The bombers had not started peeling off so there was still time.

The leading Stuka never knew where the lightning came from. With a swastika backed by a red field in his windscreen, Stan pressed the gun button and sliced through the middle of the killer, breaking it into almost two separate parts.

The Hawk faded to the right and another

Stuka rolled past him, unaware that death was dropping from the sky. Stan put her up 200 feet; and then, his motor screaming, he laid over and was upon the Stuka, his guns belching death. The bomber staggered and winged over, spilling men out of her hull like sacks out of a van.

Savagely, Stan rolled and twisted seeking another target. O'Malley had gotten into the formation first and he was taking it apart with a display of aerial gymnastics that made the Jerries forget anything but escape. Allison was cutting away far to the left and the carefully planned blitz was already a fearful rout, with death as the lot of most of the killers. Scattered, they zoomed and dived, seeking only to escape. As they went twisting out of their formations, low over the city, the cables of death claimed many victims.

Then the Spitfires of Moon Flight came roaring in from a wild chase to the east and the rout was complete. Within a few minutes the astonished gunners and the men at the lights below began to realize that somehow what had seemed certain to be a terrible *luftwaffe* had been turned into a victory.

The Ack-Ack boys laid off. Then Moon Flight plus Red Flight bored upward to see how many Messerschmitts Herr Goering had sent along as fighter planes. The ME's came cascading downward, eager to see their charges safely home. There was a flight of forty and another of fifty. They were met by three streaking silver planes that carried no dull paint and looked like commercial craft out for a spree. The three had out-climbed the Spitfires.

Stan swerved to the right to give O'Malley room. He had outflown the Irishman and was grinning. O'Malley still had a few things to learn about a Hawk before he could get everything out of his big engine. He slashed into the formation with guns raking the descending ships. Past them he flashed and bored on into the darkness. When he got back into position again, the Spitfires had arrived and the Messer-schmitts were scattering and ducking into the night.

"Calling the Hawks. Calling the Hawks," Stan called.

"Sure, an' it was a poor show," O'Malley's voice came in. "This colleen has the need of two big eyes to see where the spalpeens go when they run away.''

''This will be nice news for the Nazis to broadcast,'' Allison called.

''Moon Flight, come in. Moon Flight, come in. Enemy dispersed.'' The call was from the field below.

Then Garret's voice broke in. ''Squadron Leader of Moon Flight reporting. Enemy dispersed with many casualties. Two of our fighters left formation.''

''Bah,'' Stan heard O'Malley growl.

They went down with the Spitfires and rolled into the floodlights. The O.C. was there and very much excited. Before Stan could reach the door of the briefing room Farrell had him.

''We watched the show, what we could see of it. Those Hawks were great. But how did you come to disregard my orders as to the hour of your leaving the naval base?''

Stan smiled. ''Don't you think it lucky we did, sir?''

''It was more than lucky. Many lives would have been lost and much damage done. I'm afraid we would have come in for some stiff criticism.'' He shook his head. ''Gar-

ret gets off slow, but this is the second time
he has cleaned up.''

The O.C. hurried away, still shaking his
head. Stan barged into the room and reported as a part of Moon Flight. The briefing officer hesitated about putting down the
three Hawks.

''We have no planes of that type or
name,'' he complained.

''Step yerself out to the field an' have a
look,'' O'Malley suggested.

Stan was watching Garret narrowly. The
Squadron Leader was scowling bleakly as
he moved up to the desk. He seemed in a
great hurry. Stan kicked O'Malley on the
shin and left without filling out a report.
Allison stayed to make the regulation report
in detail and to answer questions fired at
him about the new ship. O'Malley failed to
take Stan's hint and stayed to have his say
about the Hawks.

Stan hurried to his quarters and got out of
his flying togs. He wasn't officially on duty
and he had a few things he wanted to do. He
headed along the hallway, keeping out of
sight. Garret came in and he was almost
running. He charged into his room and

Stan heard him changing clothes. Suddenly there was no sound at all from the room and Stan slipped to the door. Garret was supposed to be on duty, ready to go up again in case another raid came over. He listened carefully, then tried the knob. The door was open and he looked into the room.

What Stan saw made him shove inside at once. Garret had vanished, but in his haste he had left a trail. One window was open. Stan saw clothes tossed about showing the haste with which he had changed. He leaped to the window and slipped out, letting himself to the ground.

As he pushed aside a thick bush near the wall he saw the street dimly. There was no one on it wearing a Royal Air Force uniform. The only person on the dark street was a man in civilian clothes. Stan stared hard for a moment, then sucked in his breath and started after the man, who was sauntering swiftly into the darkness.

At the first shaded light Stan realized that the man he was trailing was Garret, and that the officer was in a big hurry. He strode along, pausing now and then to peer back and to listen. Stan used the tactics he had

learned in Colorado while hunting mule
deer. He moved when Garret moved and
stopped when Garret stopped. Sliding along
noiselessly he shifted from one patch of
black shadow to another.

Stan did not remember how many blocks
they walked, but he knew where he was in a
general way. When Garret ducked down a
flight of narrow steps, Stan moved up and
listened. The opening below was black dark.
He heard a door open but saw no light. Then
he heard a guttural voice challenging Garret. After that the door closed and there
were no other sounds.

Stan listened for a full minute. As he
stood there unmoving, a part of the black
shadow along the wall, he considered the
situation. He had left his gun in his room.
He was unarmed and those below would
have guns. A burning desire glowed within
him, a desire to have a look at the men Garret was meeting. Carefully he felt his way
down the stairs and located the door.

The knob turned soundlessly under pressure but the door was locked. Moving back
up the stairs, Stan stood looking at the old
house which rose above the basement where

Garret had entered. The house was one of a row that had been hit by several demolition bombs. Most of the upper and the first story had been wrecked and the debris had not yet been cleared away. That was strange, because most of the other houses in the row had been damaged, too, but had been repaired.

Stan moved up the front steps, picking his way through a litter of brick and broken timbers. He saw a doorway ahead, with a door sagging open upon smashed hinges. Moving slowly and carefully Stan entered the room. A pile of plaster and brick lay on the floor with some broken furniture stacked in a corner. He was about to turn away, knowing that anyone below would hear footsteps above, when he saw a beam of light coming up through the floor.

Moving very slowly he crossed to the center of the room and bent down. A torn rug lay under a pile of bricks and the rug covered a broken board in the floor. Stan got down on his hands and knees. With great care he slid the rug back a little and more light shone through the hole in the floor. Stan lay down and put his eye to the hole.

He could see very clearly everything in the basement below the wrecked house. There was a table directly under him and on it stood a portable short-wave radio sending and receiving set. A light, swung from the ceiling, flooded the table and the room.

A little hunchbacked fellow sat before the radio with earphones clamped over a shiny bald head. Three men sat across the table from the radio operator. One of them held Stan's attention. He was a short, thick-shouldered man with a bullethead that was covered with bristling, cropped hair. His eyes bulged and his mouth was a grim slash across his face. On the table at his elbow lay an English fire warden's hat. He was tapping the table with a thick finger and talking to Garret.

Garret sat beside the radioman, his face black and dour. It was plain the man had been giving Garret a tongue lashing. The other two men, seated beside the speaker, looked to Stan like London wharf rats.

"Herr Kohle, you are a blundering fool.

Seventeen bombers were lost tonight, and because you failed to do your duty. The *Kommandant* will hear of this," the bullet-headed man snarled.

"But, Herr Naggel, I followed instructions. The O.C. ordered the three to return in the morning and that order was sent to you by Mickle," Garret whined.

Stan made a note of the name Mickle. He had a hunch an orderly or a mechanic would be put on the spot once that name was traced to its owner.

"Now that the great blitzkrieg is set for an hour before daylight we cannot afford to take chances. You must do your part as planned." Herr Naggel spread a map on the table. "Here we have the concentrations of planes in Belgium, in France and in Norway. One thousand planes will come over London. There will be no city left tomorrow night. We will walk out and join the refugees pouring out of London, and then make contact with the parachute troops and the men from the gliders." He smiled wolfishly and licked his lips. "Those gliders are ready. You should see them. Three for each pilot plane and each will have its squad

of men. At 20,000 feet the pilot plane will
cut them loose and they will glide down upon
England without a sound." He laughed
softly.

"They say there will always be an England. Bah. England is done." He glared
at Garret. "When the decoy bombers come
over, you will lead your flight after them.
Now that they have increased your squadron
to twenty Spitfires, and the three American
planes, they could do much damage. With
early dawn light to fly by they might break
up the whole plan."

"I will take them on a chase that will lead
them so far away they won't get back. Send
a big flight of Messerschmitts in after my
squadron contacts the decoy bombers and
have them start a dogfight. They never quit
as long as there is anything left to fight. But
you better send plenty of fighters."

"That is planned," Naggel said gruffly.
"We cannot control the other flights that
will go up, but yours is the key defense unit,
the best they have, and it is most important
in our plans."

Stan bent forward and strained his eyes
to see the markings on the map. He wanted

to know where those three concentrations of invasion planes were. He was able to spot them because they were marked upon the map with red circles. He was pressing his face against the boards to see better when one foot slipped a little. His right boot scraped across the floor.

Naggel did not stop talking and none of the others seemed to have heard. One of the men beside Naggel lighted a cigarette and leaned back. The radioman turned a dial and began talking softly into the portable mike. Stan could not hear what he said.

Slowly Stan got to his feet. He had the information he wanted. The thing to do was to beat the Jerries to the punch. The Royal Air Force would blast every one of those air fields and get the enemy on the ground. But he had to get to headquarters at once, everything depended upon speed. Only a few hours remained for the job.

Stan slipped through the wrecked door and paused for a moment. As he started to move down the steps a dark shadow loomed behind him. Before he could leap aside a hard object crashed down upon his head. Red and white lights danced before his eyes and stabbing pains racked him. Then he slid slowly forward and fell on his face.

When Stan opened his eyes he was sitting in a chair with his head hanging on one side. He shook his head and groaned, then focused his gaze upon the leering face of Herr Naggel.

"You would listen?" Herr Naggel said slowly.

Stan said nothing. He expected no mercy from the men who had taken him prisoner. His head was splitting and he felt weak and sick. A thought stabbed through the pain. They had heard him when his foot slipped. The man at the radio had called to someone near by. His sky fighter training had been poor preparation for ground sleuthing, Stan decided.

"We will be gone in a few minutes, and when we go, we will leave a little comrade with you." Herr Naggel motioned to a large grenade sitting on the table. As Stan fixed his gaze upon the grenade he realized that the radioman had gone, and had taken the portable set with him. Garret was gone, too, and he was alone with Naggel and his two rats.

Stan made another discovery. He was not bound. Likely the spies had not had rope or wire to make him fast, or they were sure their heavy Luger pistols would keep him in his place. Herr Naggel tapped the iron case of the grenade.

"The little one cannot be kept from exploding once the pin is removed. I will pull the pin and lock the door." He smiled and his mouth twisted at the corners.

Stan rose to his feet. He was not so bad off as he had thought. Dizzy, but not out by any means. He staggered and swayed, putting on as good a show of grogginess as he could. Herr Naggel seemed to relish watching him struggle to remain on his feet.

The thing that was pounding away inside Stan's head was the question: "How long was I out? How much time have I left?" He was not thinking about the almost certain death that stared him in the face. Naggel pulled out a big silver watch and looked at it.

"Two o'clock," he muttered. "We must wait fifteen minutes."

Stan almost showed his relief. There was still time! At that moment someone in the street above began shouting and screaming.

Car brakes ground and there was a crashing noise. The blackout had claimed another victim of blind driving. Involuntarily the eyes of Herr Naggel and his men turned toward the door.

Lightning thought brought lightning action to Stan Wilson. It was no planned or prepared action, just wild, whirlwind action that was launched in the flicker of an eyebrow.

. With one hand Stan clamped down upon Herr Naggel's Luger; he lunged in close to the squat Nazi. In the same movement he sent a right smashing across to the jaw of the spy. Herr Naggel let out a gusty grunt and rocked back on his heels, then went down in a limp pile on the floor.

Jerking the Luger free, Stan swept it upon the two rats. "Down on your faces," he gritted. "Flat on the floor or I'll shoot!"

Stark fear leaped into the eyes of the two men and they tumbled flat on the floor, sprawling there with faces covered. Then Stan saw Herr Naggel pulling himself slowly up to the table. A wild, crazy light flamed in the eyes of the spy. Stan made a lightning decision.

It made his flesh creep to think of shooting these men, but he dared not leave them in the cellar, and there was nothing to bind and gag them with. If he left them, they might get away and send word through the vanished radioman to the Jerry squadrons awaiting the zero hour.

He was saved from any solution of his own planning by Herr Naggel. The spy reached over, after getting to his feet, and grasped the grenade. Jerking out the pin he hurled the grenade at Stan's head. Stan ducked and the bomb struck the wall and bounded back. It spun around and came to rest a few feet from the door.

"We all die. The plan shall not fail!" Herr Naggel screamed hoarsely.

Stan leaped over the grenade and halted before the door. He jerked at it but it was locked. There was no time to get a key from the men. Behind him he heard Naggel's insane laugh. He brought the Luger down and blasted away at the lock. It shattered and the door opened.

Stan dived into the blackness outside, kicking the door shut as he went out. He had stumbled only one step when the whole wall of the basement burst outward and he was hurled up the steps and sent sprawling out into the street.

Stan swayed, sagged forward, then pitched on his face upon the hard street. A trickle of blood ran from the corners of his mouth. His eyes closed slowly, glassily. He lay still, a twisted, inert bundle of flesh.

A few minutes later car brakes screeched and a black roadster with hooded lights came to a halt. Two police officers jumped out. The dim lights were fixed upon the body of a man lying face down in the street. They lifted Stan to his feet and revived him after a few minutes of work.

Stan blinked his eyes and took one big gulp of air. He began talking in jerky sentences, repeating over and over.

"Get me to M Section of the Royal Air Force."

"That's as close as any first aid station," one of the officers said as he looked at Stan's uniform. "And I'm thinking he belongs there."

They helped Stan into the car and sped

away. Stan wiggled his arms and legs and decided he had been hit a hard jolt in the back which had knocked the breath out of him and shocked him badly, but otherwise he was all right.

CHAPTER XI

PLENTY OF TROUBLE

STAN WILSON followed by O'Malley and Allison barged into Wing Commander Farrell's office. Before them marched Arch Garret with a Luger shoved into the small of his back. The O.C. leaped to his feet. He had been nodding in his chair and thought he must be dreaming. He quickly changed his mind.

Stan told his story in brief, clipped sentences. Farrell did not interrupt. When he had finished Garret broke in before the O.C. could say anything. He was not the defiant and arrogant lieutenant he had been. Fear showed in his eyes and his voice was shaking.

"I'll talk if it will save me from a firing squad," he begged.

"I may try but I do not think any power will save you," Farrell said sternly. "But you had better talk for the sake of your own conscience."

"They had me where they wanted me. My father was in Germany, in a concentration camp. I had to do what they ordered." Sweat was standing out in big drops on Garret's forehead. "I was straight and did my job until they got to me."

"That's why you got where you are and why you were not released after your first bad report. Your past record was fine." The O.C. dropped back into his chair. He jerked a phone from its cradle. He was looking intently at Garret as he clicked the receiver. "Go on, talk. I'll do what I can for you."

"The radioman is at 30 Elm Inn," Garret babbled. "He is to wait there for word from Herr Naggel. When Naggel gives the word, all will be clear for the attack."

"Naggel won't send any messages," Stan said grimly, remembering the terrible explosion which had blown him clear out into the street.

The O.C. had gotten his man and was barking into the phone. He kept on putting through calls and talking to Stan and Allison and O'Malley at the same time.

"Get a guard, O'Malley, and turn Garret

over to him. Wilson, stand by. Allison, get
back to the mess and see that all of the men
stand by ready for action."

Stan watched the O.C. with admiration.
He was a demon for getting things done in a
speedy and effective manner. Stan handed
his Luger to O'Malley. The Irishman
prodded Garret with it.

"Get a move on, ye skulkin' hyena,"
O'Malley growled.

They moved out of the room with O'Malley telling the wilted Garret what he thought
of him.

"We can get a crack at them before daylight, if headquarters will let us pull an im-
mediate raid." The O.C. held the receiver
jammed to his ear with one hand while he
fished into a drawer with the other. He
found a cigar and bit the end off, then
clamped the cigar between his teeth. Speak-
out of the side of his mouth, he went on.

"How did you come to bag Garret?"

"I found him in the mess, sir. He was sitting there waiting for the call to action he
was sure was coming. He had warned all of
the boys against loose flying. They had strict
orders to stick close to him," Stan said.

"This is one raid they won't put over, thanks to you, Wilson."

"We can blast them at their bases," Stan said eagerly. "They'll be grounded and waiting, saving their gas and getting ragged nerves while they wait."

"Ragged nerves?" The O.C. had his man on the phone and began barking at him, arguing furiously. He waved his cigar and pounded the desk and bellowed. Five minutes later he clamped the receiver into place and swung around to face Stan. Wiping the sweat from his face, he said:

"That was the Air Ministry."

Stan grinned. "I take it you convinced them, sir."

"Convinced them? I routed them!" Farrell found a match and lighted his frayed cigar. Getting to his feet, he added. "We're off for those bases and this time I fly myself. I have been wanting to see how this show stacks up with the last one, and now I'm going to find out."

Stan followed him out into the night. After that things happened with lightning speed. Stan lost track of all the things they did and the places they went.

First of all, the radioman was caught with all of his equipment. The hunchback cracked when faced with the grim prospect of facing a firing squad within a half-hour. His code book revealed a complicated mass of information which was deciphered at once, with some assistance from him. Exact locations were charted and objectives laid out. All of it was done on the run.

Before the officers were through with the radioman, a message was sent out to the Nazis holding up the attack until further instructions were given. The message was in code and properly sent so that it would be received by the enemy as an order from their key man in London. Herr Naggel's secret code number was signed to it.

Then there was a cold and clearheaded gathering around the big map in the central control room. Four flights would go out. Not just four ordinary flights, but four all-out invasion formations with all the punch the Royal Air Force could put behind them.

Red Flight, with its three deadly Hawks, was assigned to go with the long-range Consolidateds over France to the base from which the biggest of the Jerry bombers would take off. This would be the first wave sent over, because it had the longest route. It would be protected by the Hawks and by Defiants equipped for long-range flying. At last Stan got away from the O.C. and dashed to the mess.

He had secured three capable gunners to take along because he expected an opportunity to do some ground strafing. The early morning sky was cloudy with high fog and black clouds. If the weather held all the way over, they would be able to stage a real surprise.

In the mess he found Judd and McCumber and Kelley talking with Allison and O'Malley. Other men were gathered in small groups. The tension was high in the room.

"When do we get the signal?" Judd asked. His detail was to a field in Belgium.

"Any minute now," Stan said. He looked over Judd's head and saw that O'Malley was munching a slab of apple pie.

"Sure, an' we'll all get to go on a long vacation after this is over," O'Malley said. "There won't be a Jerry left in the sky."

Stan smiled but back of the smile there was a feeling of grimness. A lot of the eager youngsters gathered in that room would not come back.

"I'll see that you get your vacation in a pie factory," he promised.

Three sergeants came in and stood waiting. Stan went to them.

"Kent, Ames, and Martin, sir, reporting as gunners," one of the men said.

"Fine. Come along and I'll give you a one minute lesson on the guns you'll use, though you likely don't need it." He turned to Allison. "Pack out my togs, will you?"

"I'll bring a helmet and a chute," Allison drawled. "The Nazis will make it so hot for you, you won't need a fur suit."

Stan grinned in response to Allison's casual manner. Both knew this would be the most important action they had yet been engaged in, that it would be one of the most terrific and devastating raids staged during the entire war, yet it was best to kid about it. That was the only way to relieve the tension all of them were under, keep them cool and collected until the shooting actually started.

CHAPTER XII

LUFTWAFFE IN REVERSE

THE night was cloudy but there was little low fog. In a dozen scattered flight centers men were busy. Coveralled ground squads swarmed around fighter planes, medium bombers and long-range giants whose lettering B Y 3, painted there by Yank builders, had been smeared over with British lacquer. Exhausts flamed, bomb trucks trundled in and out, while pilots and gunners checked rigging and outfits. The big show was on, the biggest the Royal Air Force had ever planned.

Stan and O'Malley and Allison waited with their gunners near them. They had checked the Hendee Hawks so many times they could see every detail of the ships if they closed their eyes. O'Malley had come near being recommended for court-martial when he battled the O.C. over an order to carry extra gasoline instead of racks of bombs.

"Didn't we blow up a pocket battleship?" he argued sourly.

"After Jerry serves us up a welcome reception we'll talk," Allison said. "I'm expecting it to be hot."

At that moment the intersquadron speaker began to rattle off clipped orders. Every man was on his feet instantly. The moment had come for them to take off. Number 30 swarmed out on the field. Allison was in command again, Stan had insisted upon that arrangement. Allison was cold and calculating, Stan Wilson was a fighter and wanted action. Anyway, Allison had earned that right to lead. He was the original flight lieutenant of Red Flight.

Stan grinned eagerly as he swung himself into the cockpit and glanced back to see that his gunner got set. He called back over his shoulder. "Tight straps, Sergeant, we likely will be in a few tight spots."

"Yes, sir," the gunner answered. He settled back against his shock pad and adjusted his belt.

Strange how a fellow can always take up

another notch in his belt, Stan thought. Then he jerked the throttle open and the Hawk roared and strained on the cab rank. He pinched one brake and swung around, heading down the field with a finger of light guiding them.

"Red Flight, check your temperatures. Red Flight, are you set?" Allison's voice was crisp and metallic.

Stan and O'Malley cleared and the Hawks swung around. The recording officer and the coveralled mechanics had slipped back into the darkness. A mobile floodlight thumped over the black field ahead, took position, and a yellow shaft of light slapped down the field. The adjustment was made on the shadow bar and the three Hawks nosed into the band of black and waited, trembling, ready.

The signal came from the recording officer's Aldis light and they were off. Screeching into the night, twisting up the glory trail with the hydrogen gorged balloons tugging at their cables, waiting like gloating monsters for their victims, out of the notch and up they went.

"Tight formation," Allison droned. And Stan in the right-hand slot shoved in closer to the roaring monster in the lead.

"Contacting Liberators," Allison drawled.

Stan looked out and saw the dull forms of the thirty ton battle cruisers of the air sliding along below. The big fellows were cutting through the night at a terrific pace considering their pay loads and their own weight. Their 4,800 horsepower hurled them on at a pace that made the Spitfires and the Defiants hustle.

Red Flight took its place high above the drifting Liberators. Below would be the Defiants and on each side the Spitfires and Hurricanes. It was a big show and would soon be on.

"St. Omer with the field at Astree Blanche as the objective," Stan muttered to himself. This was a change in plans made after a careful study of the hunchback's little book. It would not be so bad as flying deep into Nazi country.

"Heather Raid," Stan muttered and grinned. The High Command was sending a great flight of bombers and fighters to blast enemy positions and they called it Heather Raid.

"Heather Raid—Heather Raid—rendezvous—zero hour." That was the Squadron Leader. Stan watched and listened. Nothing more came in and Allison kept flying straight ahead.

They were drifting along above the clouds. There was a moon and plenty of stars. The pale light made the squadron look like a school of fishes swimming through a blue-black sea. The clouds would be fine for everyone but the Jerries. Down below the Hurricanes would be slipping in and out of the clouds, watching, taking bearings, whispering up to the giants above, telling them what they couldn't see.

"Red Flight, go down. Yellow Flight up." The Squadron Leader spoke tersely as though he had sighted enemy planes coming up.

Stan peeled off and went down, with Allison and O'Malley trailing into formation. They hit the clouds, punched through and saw lights winking below. They were solitary lights and revealed little. Perhaps they were ship's lights on the channel. Then they went back up through the clouds and took a place below the Liberators. Stan glanced up at the big ships. The British had changed the name of those Consolidated B Y 3's to Liberator. It was a proper change, Stan thought.

Suddenly a bank of cloud on the right and above was lighted with a red glow. A second later a Messerschmitt One-Ten came flaming down, tossing away parts as it spun. A broken Defiant followed it down in a wide, agonizing spiral.

"What goes on up there?" Stan called back to his gunner.

"Upper level defense units in contact, sir," the gunner answered. He had been on thirty-six raids across the channel and knew what to expect.

"And they pulled us down to let the Defiants have the fun," Stan muttered.

"Have a look, Red Flight," Allison's voice snapped.

Down the Hawks went for a look at the ground. They saw a band of light swing across the ground, then steady.

"Landing field lights located, port a few points," Allison droned.

Almost at once the Liberators changed their tone. They began to growl and roar. Positions were taken and the Hawks slid up to be above the bombers, out of their way and into the path of diving Messerschmitts and Heinkels. But the lone fighter seemed to be the only enemy ship in the air.

As Stan watched the action he realized that bombing wasn't just releasing a stick or two of bombs. Its complications were apparent. Far below them the earth had suddenly begun to erupt fire and flame. They were clear of the clouds and their objective was below, a circle inside a ring of flaming guns all pointed at the bombers. And the Liberators were going down with feathered propellers.

Twelve thousand feet below lay their objective. The bombers were in a big hurry to catch the rows of black planes on the ground, to spot the oil reserves and to smash the surface of the runways. They slipped away in screaming dives and left Red Flight to watch from above.

Tracer bullets trailed threads of fire up-

Up they went, nosing through the flaming muck. This time they had little trouble in breaking through. Great holes and spaces in the barrage showed where the bombers had spotted gun placements. O'Malley was on Stan's left now and Stan was flying the center slot. There had been no time to take regulation position. Stan saw O'Malley's Hawk lift and shear away from a blasting burst of steel as a shell exploded under her. An instant later he knew the Hawk had picked up a package of death. It was twisting and wobbling, but going on up.

"Go in, O'Malley! Go in, O'Malley," Allison was droning. "Get back across. Get back across."

Before Stan could do anything at all, he was up through the muck, and then through the clouds, into a real battle. The sky was full of twisting, diving planes, all spitting at each other in deadly fashion. He was so busy keeping Messerschmitts off his tail that he lost track of Allison and O'Malley. He noted that there were only a few Spitfires and Defiants near him, though the air was literally filled with Jerries. It dawned on him that they might wish to force down this new plane so as to have a look at it. And he wasn't able to get a single swastika inside his sight circle. Suddenly he heard a familiar voice calling:

"Heather Raid, come in. Objective successfully attacked. Heather Raid, come in."

"Good idea," Stan agreed. He laid over and sliced into a mass of Messerschmitts ahead of him, opening his throttle wide and cutting in his booster. As he bored into the formation it opened to let him go through. Only one ME failed to give way. It roared straight at him as though bent upon ramming him. Stan's lips pulled into a tight line and he reached for his gun button.

"Sorry, feller," he muttered. "But you don't ram me."

He pressed the button but no burst answered. He was out of ammunition. With a yank he pulled the Hawk up, then twisted her over. The hair at the back of his neck lifted as his understructure raked across the hatch cover of the Jerry. Lead streamed below him as he flashed past.

Stan kicked off his booster and headed for home. The Messerschmitts gave chase but they slipped away from them as easily as a swallow would outdistance a plover. Behind him he heard his gunner laughing.

"What's up?" he called back.

"I touched up that Jerry who tried to ram us, sir," the sergeant answered. "Potted his rudder and you should see him do stunts."

Stan had completely forgotten he carried a gunner. The man had been silent all of the time. Now Stan knew he must have been giving an account of himself.

"How did you make out?" he asked.

"Fine, sir. I believe I made several hits."

A short while later they circled above their home field and came in. Lights blazed on the field for the first time since Stan had been flying from it. Number 30 would be lighted up for an hour at least, in spite of raiders. This was by way of celebrating their victory.

Stan climbed out of his plane. He saw Allison coming across the field. They met and Stan could think of nothing to say. O'Malley hadn't come in.

"Tough, O'Malley missing that big fight after the raid," he finally said.

Allison looked at him. A slow smile came to his lips. He pointed out across the field.

Stan looked and saw a mass of twisted wreckage. What certainly was the tail assembly of a Hendee Hawk was sticking out of the twisted mass.

"He parked that mess there, then climbed out and walked into the briefing room," Allison said. "We'll find him in there grousing because they called us in before we got all of those Messerschmitts."

Stan's laugh rang out and he made for the briefing room. Sure enough, O'Malley was there and he was fuming.

" 'Tis time I quit this job," he shouted at the briefing officer. "When a man can't stay an' settle an argument like a gentleman, 'tis time to quit."

The officer grinned at O'Malley. Stan slapped his pal on the back. "I'll buy you a pie, and darned if I don't eat one myself."

O'Malley considered this for a moment, then said: "If a man can't fight, then the next best thing is to consider a bit of food."

Arm in arm the three fliers of Red Flight walked into the mess.

The next morning Allison and O'Malley and Stan were eating breakfast at a side table. Allison had been over to headquarters and he had learned a few things. Over bacon and hot cakes he told them what he had heard.

"Garret was the man on the spot, but they got a fellow who was way up, they wouldn't give his name. He kept Garret from getting tossed out of the service and worked it so he was made a Squadron Leader. They planned to get a man like Garret into every squadron if they could."

" 'Tis black, the likes of such a man is," O'Malley said with a scowl.

"Garret admitted bleeding Stan's gas tank and leading Moon Flight off the trail. I asked him how he found out Stan was a Yank and he said the information was sent him from the Nazi secret service." Allison leaned back and smiled. "I have an idea our Intelligence will do a lot more snooping from now on."

"Sure an' 'tis a nice tale, but one we already had figured out," O'Malley said.

"I got a real raking for not turning over Stan's record to Farrell as soon as we were transferred," Allison said with a grin. "I now tender my apologies but, after the first spoofing I did, I clean forgot about those reports. They didn't seem important. Stan is one of the best pilots in the Royal Air Force, and what we need is fighters."

"It's all over now, and I accept your apology," Stan said.

O'Malley scowled suddenly. "Do you gents think we'll ever get to see any more action? I bet we won't."

He was answered by the intersquadron speaker. It began rasping:

"Red Flight, all out. Red Flight, all out. Bandits sighted over the Dover coast. Heavy fighter escort of Messerschmitt One-Tens."

THE END

Watch for the next Air Combat story!

TED SCOTT FLYING STORIES

By FRANKLIN W. DIXON

Illustrated. Every Volume Complete in Itself.

You'll like Ted Scott. He's a daring young American whose feats of flying thrill the whole world, but with it all he keeps a level head on his shoulders. The whole flying series has been inspired by recent aerial exploits and is dedicated to Lindbergh, Commander Byrd, Clarence Chamberlin and other heroes of the skies.

OVER THE OCEAN TO PARIS
RESCUED IN THE CLOUDS
OVER THE ROCKIES WITH THE AIR MAIL
FIRST STOP HONOLULU
THE SEARCH FOR THE LOST FLYERS
SOUTH OF THE RIO GRANDE
ACROSS THE PACIFIC
THE LONE EAGLE OF THE BORDER
FLYING AGAINST TIME
OVER THE JUNGLE TRAILS
LOST AT THE SOUTH POLE
THROUGH THE AIR TO ALASKA
FLYING TO THE RESCUE
DANGER TRAILS OF THE SKY
FOLLOWING THE SUN SHADOW
BATTLING THE WIND
BRUSHING THE MOUNTAIN TOP
CASTAWAYS OF THE STRATOSPHERE

GROSSET & DUNLAP   *Publishers*   NEW YORK